This Weather
of Ours

Photograph by E. L. Hawke.

GREAT SNOWSTORM OF JANUARY 1940.

A fifteen feet snowdrift on January 30, 1940, on the Berkhamsted-
Dunstable road across the Chiltern Hills, near Dagnall.

This Weather of Ours

BY
ARNOLD B. TINN
F.R.MET.S.

LONDON
GEORGE ALLEN & UNWIN LTD

FIRST PUBLISHED 1946
SECOND EDITION 1949
All rights reserved

To my friend

BASIL W. LEE

PRINTED IN GREAT BRITAIN BY
THE BLACKFRIARS PRESS LTD.
LEICESTER

CONTENTS

ILLUSTRATIONS

LIST OF TABLES

FOREWORD

My aim in writing this book is to give a picture of the weather over the British Isles for those who are interested in it—and who is not?—and at the same time offering groundwork for the student who wishes to make a more intimate study of the interesting subject.

When I became interested in the weather I discovered that though one could obtain books on meteorology in general, it was not so easy to find one dealing in more detail with the climate and weather of our own islands.

I wished to know how conditions varied up and down Britain; how my favourite resorts compared with others; how the weather programme in the wind-swept Hebrides contrasted with the placidity of the Thames Valley.

Someone once told me that where I lived the summers were hotter and the winters colder than anywhere else in England. This was untrue and absurd, like so many other things one is told about the weather, or any other subject. I wanted the facts. I wanted to know, too, what could happen when it was very cold or very hot, very wet or very dry. I wanted to discover how much, in exceptional circumstances, the weather could diverge from the average.

As many other people are interested in these and other questions I have tried to answer them in this book. It is the book I have long wanted to read. I hope that you will want to read it too.

I am grateful to the Director of the Meteorological Office and the Controller of His Majesty's Stationery Office for their kindness in allowing me to make use of official data published in the Monthly Weather Report, British Rainfall, the Meteorological Magazine, and the Book of Normals of Meteorological Elements; and also to the Royal Meteorological Society for using information contained in the Quarterly Journal. I am indebted, too, to those research workers whose investigations and experiments are continually extending the limits of our knowledge.

ARNOLD B. TINN.

CHAPTER I.

May I Introduce Our British Weather?

Every day the sequence of weather changes passes before our eyes. Sir Napier Shaw has well described weather as a drama. The performance is continuous, and as it takes place on our own doorsteps there is no charge for admission. We may view the show from a comfortable seat through the window, or we may step outside on to the stage and share things more intimately.

The ordinary spectator, however, misses a great deal. He is like a person who has entered the theatre in the middle of a play and wonders what it is all about. Only when we know something about the weather can we really enjoy it, and if we miss the enjoyment of the never-ceasing parade of weather changes we are missing much of our own lives. The science of meteorology, which deals with climate and weather, is a complex one owing to the vastness of the forces involved. Fortunately, it is not necessary for us to have a knowledge of complicated technicalities in order to appreciate weather. All we need is an insight into the broad factors which govern it.

Where does our weather come from? Is it manufactured on the premises or do we import it? Open an atlas and look at the position of the British Isles. We can see that these islands are on the western edge of the great Eurasian land mass stretching from the shores of the Atlantic Ocean to Vladivostok, a distance of roughly 6,500 miles. To the westwards are the restless waves of that mighty expanse of water which separates Europe from America. These two factors are antagonistic. The great land mass to the east tends to make our climate drier, our winters colder and our summers warmer, but the influence of the Atlantic is towards a wetter climate, with milder winters and cooler summers.

For most of the time the latter influence is predominant and, as a result, we experience weather that is rarely very hot or very cold, and rainfall is sufficient at all seasons. The Atlantic Ocean should have a high place in our affections, because from its broad surface streams the south-west winds which in winter give our

islands a higher mean temperature than any other countrv in a
similar or higher latitude.

Everyone has heard of the Gulf Stream's effect on our climate.
Perhaps we have heard too much. The Gulf Stream pours its
warm waters from the Gulf of Mexico into the Atlantic, but does
it ever reach our shores? If it did the water would have ample
time to cool on its long journey. The prevailing winds over the
North Atlantic are from the south-west. These winds produce
a north-easterly drift of surface water from warm latitudes which
reaches the shores of the British Isles and western Europe to
beyond the Arctic Circle. Thus the seaports of the extreme north
of Norway and Murmansk are free from serious ice in winter,
while the Baltic ports of Germany, more than a thousand miles
further south, may be closed to navigation. This drift of warm
water, combined with mild winds in winter, would still occur
were the Gulf Stream non-existent, and it is highly probable that
our climate would then be very similar to that now experienced.

Our climate is governed by the sequence of what are called
depressions and anticyclones, the former bringing unsettled and
often rainy weather to our shores and the latter fair weather with
little or no rain, though cloud may sometimes be abundant. In
a depression the wind more or less rotates, or flows inwards, to a
centre where the barometer is lowest. These winds flow in an
anti-clockwise direction. In an anti-cyclone the barometer, or
pressure, is highest in the centre and the winds flow outwards in
a clockwise direction. The North Atlantic is the birth-place of the
depressions which bring us our rain, and they usually move
towards Britain along a north-easterly path.

As a rule, the centres of the depressions pass to our north, giving
us a mild, muggy air from the south-west, but sometimes the centre
is to the south, passing, say, up the English Channel or the Bristol
Channel. Raw, cold rain, and perhaps snow in winter, then falls.

The movement of depressions and anticyclones is very
important when we wish to peer into the future, as we shall see
in Chapter XXIV. For the time being it is enough to remember
that depressions are bad weather areas and anticyclones localities
of generally fair dry weather.

As the movements of the barometer vary with the approach or
retreat of these systems that instrument is essential if we wish to
follow our day to day weather changes. We must therefore know
what a barometer is and what it can tell us. If we regard it merely

as a piece of furniture for the entrance hall at which we occasionally glance and tap, we shall never be much the wiser. What does the barometer really do? It simply measures the pressure of the atmosphere. This must not be confused with wind pressure. Atmospheric pressure is often low when wind pressure is high, and near the centre of an anticyclone where atmospheric pressure is high, wind pressure may be almost zero.

If a glass tube about 36 inches long, sealed at one end, is filled with mercury and inverted in a cistern containing mercury it will be noticed that some of the mercury leaves the tube, causing a vacuum at the top. The column of mercury remaining will be found to be about 30 inches long, and the weight of this mercury is equivalent to the pressure of the atmosphere, or nearly fifteen pounds per square inch. This apparatus is a barometer in a crude form. In an intense depression the mercury column may be only 28 inches long, and in an unusually intense anticyclone it may rise to 31 inches.

We speak of an atmospheric pressure of 30 inches as an average one in England. This terminology is incongruous. Pressure should be measured in weight. To speak of pressure in inches is really as absurd as talking of distance in pints. To obviate this, meteorologists have adopted the millibar as the unit of pressure. A millibar is the thousandth part of a "bar," and a bar is equal to a pressure of one million dynes per square centimetre. A dyne is the physicist's unit of force and is defined as the force which produces unit acceleration in one gramme. As the force of gravity is the most familiar of all forces it is useful to remember that the force of one dyne differs little from the weight of one milligramme. The "bar" is equal to a pressure of 29.531in. of mercury at a temperature of 32° F. in latitude 45. A barometer reading of 30 inches would be shown as 1016 millibars. A low barometer of 29 inches and a high one of 30.5 inches would be 982 and 1033 millibars respectively. Pressure is shown in millibars on all modern weather charts.

The barometer used in meteorological observations is a mercury one and a miracle of accuracy. Most barometers in the home are aneroids. These have no mercury and depend upon the movements of a metal box which is a partial vacuum. It is compact and less fragile than the expensive mercury barometer. Most aneroids are graduated in inches from something under 28 inches to a little above 31 inches. They often bear intriguing legends such as Stormy, Rain, Set Fair. Ignore these decorations. If our weather was only stormy when the barometer fell to this word we should have a very placid climate, and if it only rained when the index was at Rain this country would soon become a desert. The movements of the barometer tell us whether unsettled "depression" weather or fine anticyclonic conditions are approaching or in the ascendant.

We can now consider the various items which make up our weather programme, such as rainfall, temperature, wind, humidity, fog, cloud, sunshine, snow, hail and thunder. We shall learn how and when they occur, and how and why they vary in different parts of our islands. A physical map shows how wonderfully varied Britain is, and this lavish display in a small area not only gives us our splendid scenery but is responsible for local variations of climate. Mountains, moorlands, plains, estuaries, high rocky coasts and low sandy ones, the small islands round our coast, all have their own characteristic types of weather. The same depressions move majestically over them, the same anticyclones may rest benignly on them, but each snatches something peculiar to itself. A depression passing by the mountains of Snowdonia gives very different weather than the same "low" over the flat plains of Eastern England.

What is the main feature of British weather? Is it rain? Rain fills our rivers, gives us our water supply and vitally affects the growth of our crops. It makes a green glory of our country-side in spring, but it can also make a sodden misery of a garden-party. Is England a rainy country? It is not when we compare it with some other lands. London's rainfall of 25 inches a year is less than that of Rome with 32 inches, Florence with 35 inches, or Nice with 31 inches. Across the Atlantic, New York has 42 inches. Many of us think of Rome and Nice as having less rain than London; many more think it is always raining in Manchester. It is time we examined the facts.

CHAPTER II.

RAIN DOES HAVE METHOD

IN our climate sunshine is popular, but rain, at least with town-dwellers, is not. The old nursery rhyme of "Rain, rain, go to Spain," would be welcomed in many parts of the Iberian peninsula, were it true. In Britain we are spared the horrors of prolonged drought.

Where does our rain come from? The air always contains moisture, even on very dry days. In the main, this comes from evaporation over the oceans. Just as blood circulates through the human body, so in nature moisture has its own process of circulation. The sun's heat evaporates water from the ocean and the wind carries it as vapour over the land. When the air can hold no more invisible moisture clouds form and ultimately rain occurs. Some of the rain sinks into the ground and feeds vegetation; some evaporates again into the air; some percolates through the subsoil to form springs and underground reservoirs; much flows off the ground, down the hills into the valleys to form streams and rivers, which in their turn carry the water back to its mother ocean.

Rain is measured by a gauge of simple but accurate design. A circular funnel, five or eight inches in diameter, catches the rain and passes it to an inner can. Every morning, usually at 9 a.m., the gauge is inspected and any water measured in a graduated glass. The unit of measurement is .01 inch, and if there is less than half of this the word "trace" is entered in the register. A standard rain gauge is shown in Figure 1. Special gauges are used in mountain areas where the fall is very heavy.

Anyone can construct a simple rough gauge from an ordinary metal funnel fitted into a bottle. By calculating the area of the circular mouth of the funnel by the formula πr^2 where r is the radius and π is 3.1416, and then using a test-tube as a measuring glass after estimating the relation between the area of the mouth of the funnel and the area of the bore of the test-tube.

The process of rainfall depends on the natural law that warm air can contain much more water-vapour than cold air. Air at a temperature of 70°F. when saturated contains four times as much water-vapour as does an equal volume of saturated air at 32°F. Chilling damp air frees the moisture to form clouds and rain. In nature this is caused when air ascends to higher levels. Air chilled at ground level produces, not rain, but mist, fog and dew.

Rain can be divided into three types—depression, convection and orographic rain. Depression rain forms the bulk of the rainfall in the lowlands. This is the rain accompanying a falling barometer as a storm system sweeps in from the Atlantic, and

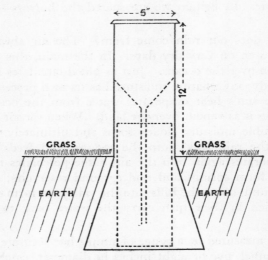

FIG. 1. RAIN GAUGE.

its steady drip from a leaden sky is characteristic of a wet day. Convective rain is equally well known. It is thunderstorm rain produced by the cooling of warm moist air rising rapidly from hot ground. We shall consider this more fully in Chapter V. Orographic rain is the term given to rain produced by moist air being cooled as it rises when meeting hills and mountains, or ascends a rising valley. This type of rain, therefore, is heaviest in mountainous districts such as Wales, the Pennines, the Lake District and the Scottish Highlands. Depression rain and orographic rain fall together in such districts, but orographic rain sometimes falls alone. It is common knowledge that hilly districts are more rainy than the plains. One hears it said that the cold mountain sides condense the moisture and cause rain.

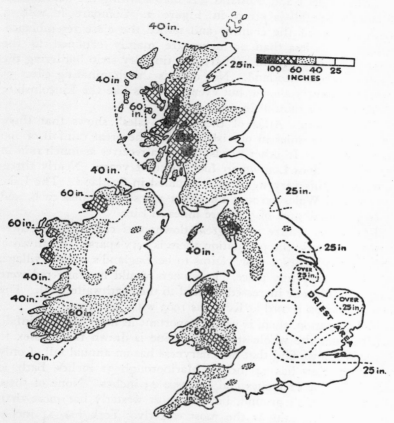

FIG. 2. ANNUAL RAINFALL. ADAPTED FROM "RAINFALL ATLAS OF THE BRITISH ISLES."

This is untrue and a fallacy. The temperature of mountain sides is very much the same as that of the air blowing over them. It is the chilling of the air as it is lifted which produces the precipitation. Even small hills produce some orographic rain. At Nottingham the rainfall near the River Trent at an altitude of 80 feet is 22½ inches per annum, but only six miles to the north on Cockpit Hill (500 feet) the fall is 28 inches. One may regard the extra 5½ inches as orographic rain.

The British Isles have remarkable variations in rainfall, ranging from a minimum of about 20 inches a year on the shores of the Thames Estuary to about 200 inches in the wettest spots of Wales, the Lake District and Scotland. A map showing the distribution of annual rainfall is given in Figure 2. Compare it with a physical map of the country and notice the close resemblance. Districts with less than 25 inches are mainly confined to the eastern half of England. There is a tiny dry strip bordering the Moray Firth in Scotland. Not only is the dominating effect of high land clearly shown, but even low hills like the Lincolnshire Wolds increase rainfall in some degree.

The "Rainfall Atlas of the British Isles" shows that there are 987 square miles in our islands with the great rainfall of 100 inches or over. In other words, this area receives as much rain in one year as does London in four to eight years. Nearly three-quarters of this very wet area is situated in Scotland. The Lake District and Wales account for about 120 square miles each, and there is a small area of 7 square miles in Eire.

Few of us realize what great downpours can occur in these localities because the population there is very sparse. Seathwaite, with its 129 inches a year, claims to be England's wettest village, but it is a very tiny place. Londoners would be staggered were their rainfall to be increased fivefold to the Seathwaite total. The wettest year on record at Kew was 1903 with 38 inches.

Configuration, then, is vastly important in its effect on rainfall, but it is not the whole story. If a line is drawn from Essex to South Wales we find that Shoeburyness has an annual fall of only 19 inches, Kew has 24 inches, Marlborough 31 inches, Bath 30 inches, Cardiff 42 inches and Swansea 45 inches. None of these places is on high ground, but the most westerly has more than twice as much rain as the most easterly. York has 24 inches and Blackpool 33 inches. Rain increases from east to west quite apart from physical features. This is not surprising, as most of our rain arrives from the Atlantic.

The east coast is the driest coast, and everyone knows the slogan, "Come to the drier side of Britain." The eastern half of the south coast has less rain than the western, and typical of this is Brighton with an annual fall of 28 inches, Bournemouth 32 inches, Torquay 33 inches, Plymouth 37 inches, and Falmouth 44 inches.

And what of Manchester? This city is proverbially notorious.

"It's always raining in Manchester." Is it true, or just a fallacy? The annual rainfall at Whitworth Park, Manchester, is 32 inches. Compare this with the average for other places in the district. Oldham averages 39 inches and Rochdale 44 inches. Liverpool has 33 inches, and Southport 32 inches. Southport has the same rainfall as Manchester, but no one talks about continuous rain there. That coastal valhalla of so many people, Bournemouth, has the same rainfall as Manchester, and Torquay is virtually the same. Famous resorts like Falmouth, Penzance or Ilfracombe have more rain than Manchester. But perhaps rain is more frequent in Manchester. Statistics show that Manchester experiences some rain on 195 days a year. So does Southport and Falmouth. There is another possibility. The rain at Manchester may fall for a greater number of hours than at other places. There is a special gauge for recording the actual time during which rain falls, but not many of these are in use, though the number is growing. At Manchester no record is kept, but just outside at Barton Airport a gauge gives an average of 680 hours of rain a year over a five year period. This is certainly slightly more than the average of 615 hours at Southport, but well below the averages of 790 hours at Falmouth and 800 hours at Huddersfield.

The traditional raininess of Manchester is a myth. Indeed, Manchester's rainfall is an average one for England as a whole. How has this legend arisen? The writer suggests that the greyness of Manchester's sky may have a good deal to do with it. The average duration of sunshine is 967 hours per annum at Oldham Road and 1,029 hours at Whitworth Park. According to official records these are the smallest known sunshine averages in England, though Bolton with 1,032 hours is virtually identical. On the other hand, Southport and Blackpool enjoy 1,500 hours of sun a year, Falmouth 1,710 hours and Bournemouth 1,760 hours. Sunshine has a tonic effect on the mind. Two places with the same rainfall, one with a poor sunshine record and the other with a good one, will appear very different. Nevertheless, the tradition of Manchester's raininess will probably live for many years yet, for there is something in human nature which prefers a fairy story to a fact.

Although the rainfall in our wettest spots may be from six to ten times that of our driest, the difference in the number of rain days is very much smaller. Rain falls on 180 days at York and 165 days in London in a year. The smallest frequency is 150 to

B

155 days round the Thames Estuary. Even if it rained every day
in the year in wet areas no place could have much more than twice
the number of rain days of the driest. Few districts have more
than 250 rain days per annum and these are in the north-west.

Compare London with its 24 inches and 165 rain days with
Glenleven, in Argyll, which receives 84 inches and 266 rain days
on an average. This gives .145 inch of rain per rain day in
London and .316 inch at Glenleven, so that one is tempted to infer
that it rains more than twice as heavily in the latter than in the
former. This is untrue. It leaves out the question of rainfall
duration. Blackwater Dam, Glenleven, has the greatest average
rainfall duration of any place for which values are at present available, totalling 1,560 hours of rain a year. This is more than 4¼
hours a day, compared with 450 hours, or about 1¼ hours a day,
at Kew. These figures reveal the fact that the average rate of
fall of rain per hour is virtually the same at Glenleven and Kew,
.054 inch. This is astonishing, and may provoke the protest, "But
it simply pours in the Highlands." So it does, sometimes, but on
the whole the heavy mountain downpours are more marked by
persistency than by great intensity. Over most of the British Isles
the average rate of rainfall is from .045 inch to .055 inch per
hour. Cwm Dyli, at the foot of Snowdon, appears to have about
twice this intensity, and other very wet spots might show a
similar increase were data available. Two points should be borne
in mind, however. In mountainous districts frequent drizzle
would reduce the average intensity of rainfall, and in the lowlands
thunder rains in summer increase the average intensity. It is
reasonable to assume, therefore, that while on a wet day in the
highlands the rain falls with considerable severity, it is not as
intense as that of a lowland thunderstorm.

What are the greatest and least amounts of rainfall that have
ever been recorded in the British Isles in a year? As much as 240
inches were measured in 1872, 1898, 1909 and 1923. In 1923 as
much as 247.3 inches fell at the Stye, Borrowdale, Cumberland,
one of the highest totals ever reported in our islands. At the
other extreme, in 1921, Margate totalled 9.29 inches for the year.
This is the only occasion when as little as ten inches has been
recorded anywhere in this country. If such conditions persisted
the countryside would rapidly become semi-desert.

In every year from 1911 to 1938 some locality reported at least
120 inches, and during the same 28 years a fall of less than 20

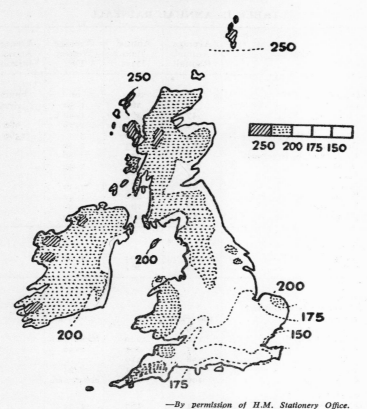

—*By permission of H.M. Stationery Office.*

FIG. 3. ANNUAL NUMBER OF RAIN DAYS (FROM THE MAP BY DR. J. GLASSPOOLE), "BRITISH RAINFALL, 1926."

inches was registered somewhere in 23 years. On an average, rainfall in a year may be expected to range from 185 inches at the wettest place to about 18 inches in the driest. The "Rainfall Atlas" shows that of the total area of 121,120 square miles of the British Isles, 69,543 square miles have less than 40 inches of rain per annum, and 51,577 square miles have more. Most of our population is found in districts with less than 40 inches. Areas with 60 inches or more are sparsely inhabited. The average annual rainfall over England is 33 inches, over Ireland 43 inches, and in Wales and Scotland 50 inches. For the British Isles as a whole the value is 41 inches.

Most of us do not possess a rain-gauge, and probably fre-

TABLE I.—ANNUAL RAINFALL

Place	Average Annual Rainfall	Annual Rain Days	Average Wettest Day	Average Annual Duration
	in.	days	in.	hours
SCOTLAND				
Lerwick	38	260	1.30	
Stornoway	47	263	1.46	
Aberdeen	30	214	1.26	680
Glenleven, Argyll	84	266	3.5	1560
Ben Nevis	161	263	4.96	
Loch Quoich, Inverness	111	245	3.86	
Inverness	27	209	1.49	
Perth	31	172	1.23	
Dundee	26	183	1.39	
Rothesay	49	228	1.42	
Edinburgh	26	189	1.26	
Glasgow	37	202	1.39	
ISLE OF MAN				
Douglas	41	204	1.68	
Ramsey	44	203		
ENGLAND				
Uplands—Lake District				
Borrowdale	100—200		4 to 5 in.	
Seathwaite	129			
Dungeon Ghyll	110	220	about 4 in.	
Keswick	55	209	2.50	
Kendal	58	210		
Ambleside	75	221	3.25	
Buttermere	106	227	about 4 in.	
Pennines				
Harrogate	31	183	1.34	
Huddersfield	34	197	1.34	800
Bradford	34	195	1.39	
Sheffield	30	182	1.35	
Buxton	48	211	1.50	
Matlock	34	189		
Leeds	24	180		
Stonyhurst	47	206	1.61	
Bolton	43	211	1.44	820
Rochdale	44	216		
Oldham	39	219		
Macclesfield	34	194	1.42	
Princetown, Dartmoor	82	220		
Lowlands				
Newcastle	26	170		
Durham	25	190	1.41	
Carlisle	32	200		
Whitehaven	44	201		
Appleby	35	214	1.43	

TABLE I.—ANNUAL RAINFALL—*continued*

Place	Average Annual Rainfall	Annual Rain Days	Average Wettest Day	Average Annual Duration
ENGLAND, *Lowlands*—contd.	in.	days	in	hours
Scarborough	26	190	1.26	
York	24	179	1.25	
Hull	25	193	1.28	
Spurn Head	23	168	1.22	
Goole	23	165		
Morecambe	37	195		
Lancaster	41	207	1.56	735
Blackpool	33	193		
Southport	32	189	1.26	615
Liverpool	33	194	1.19	
Manchester	32	195	1.19	
Derby	26	173		
Nottingham	24	178	1.27	440
Cleethorpes	24	177	1.26	
Lincoln	23	171		
Skegness	23	162	1.09	
Leicester	24	168		
Belvoir Castle	25	205	1.39	
Leamington	24	162		
Rugby	26	164	1.29	
Shrewsbury	22	166	1.29	
Stafford	27	182		
Worcester	25	170	1.26	
Birmingham	28	181	1.35	
Ross-on-Wye	28	188	1.42	465
Oundle	22	175	1.09	
Cromer	24	173	1.23	
Norwich	26	201	1.19	
Cambridge	22	163	1.22	
Shoeburyness	19	149	0.97	
Cheltenham	27	179	1.49	
Oxford	25	168	1.30	
London (Kew)	24	167	1.26	448
Reading	25	153	1.17	
Margate	23	166	1.18	
Tunbridge Wells	27	173	1.33	
Eastbourne	31	165	1.46	535
Brighton	28	163	1.45	
Southampton	31	174	1.46	
Bournemouth	32	168	1.32	
Ventnor, Isle of Wight	29	173	1.57	
Marlborough	31	186	1.34	
Bath	30	180	1.32	
Ilfracombe	37	191	1.46	
Torquay	33	174	1.38	
Plymouth	37	189	1.48	715
Falmouth	44	207	1.61	790
Penzance	41	210		
Scilly Isles	32	207	1.30	
CHANNEL ISLANDS				
Jersey	30	199	1.42	
Guernsey	33	200	1.54	

TABLE I.—ANNUAL RAINFALL—*continued*

Place	Average Annual Rainfall	Annual Rain Days	Average Wettest Day	Average Annual Duration
	in.	days	in.	hours
WALES				
Snowdon Area	118	235	4.5	1210
Llandudno	28	193	1.19	
Holyhead	35	201	1.42	680
Aberystwyth	46	209	1.26	
Welshpool	30	188	1.38	
Cardiff	42	196	1.76	715
Swansea	45	215	1.65	730
Tenby	41	200		
NORTH IRELAND				
Armagh	32	215	1.34	815
Belfast	35	214		
EIRE				
Dublin	26	198	1.50	
Birr	33	211	1.37	
Valentia	56	252	1.73	

quency of rain makes a greater impression on our minds than amount. A day with rain is defined as one on which the fall is .01 inch or more. Many "rain days" have trifling amounts. Most of England has fewer than 200 rain days a year. Figure 3 shows their distribution. The South Midlands and much of Eastern England south of the Wash has less than 175 rain days. Localities with over 200 days are the Peak of Derbyshire, East Lancashire, West Yorkshire, the Lake District, most of Scotland and Ireland, and high ground in Devon and Cornwall. Small areas in Scotland have over 250 days. Stornoway averages 263 rain days and Lerwick 260. Over a period of 20 years Baltasound, in Unst, in the extreme north of the Shetlands, averaged 296 days with rain, or only 69 days a year free from some precipitation. Most people in England groan if a single month has 25 rain days. Can one imagine the pungency of their comments if this went on interminably.

In individual years a place or two may report 300 rain days. In 1923, Creggan Reservoir, Londonderry, registered 317 days, and Baltasound aggregated 318 rain days in both 1934 and 1935. The latter place had rain on 938 out of 1,095 days in 1933-1935.

It is worth noticing that these cases of very *frequent* rain occur at places where the *amounts* are not specially great. Creggan

Reservoir, Londonderry, averages 52 inches a year, and Baltasound a comparatively modest 42 inches. Obviously there must be a good deal of light drizzle, as well as a lack of heavy thunder rains.

It is rare for less than 100 days with rain to occur anywhere in a year, but in 1921 Chatteris, Cambridgeshire, had 93, and Birchington, Kent, only 84.

As the frequency of rain days is greatest in the north-west and least in the south-east it follows that we may expect to find the longest periods of successive rain days in the former area, and the longest droughts, as a rule, in the latter.

In the island of Islay, off the West Coast of Scotland, rain was measured every day from August 12th to November 8th, 1923, a sequence of 89 rain days, or virtually a quarter of the year. The average rainfall on this island is 49 inches, a very moderate one for Western Scotland, but the island is right in the path of rain-bearing winds. During this spell of 89 days 27.77 inches fell, or an average of .31 inch per day.

The Meteorological Office recognises two types of drought in this country (a) the absolute drought (15 or more successive days without rain) and (b) the partial drought (29 or more successive days with a total fall not averaging more than .01 inch per day). The shortest and wettest partial drought possible under this definition is thus 29 days with a total fall of not more than .29 inch.

In 1938 a remarkable absolute drought of 38 days was recorded at Fort William, Wigtonshire, and Limerick (April 3 to May 10), and 37 days at Nottingham. In the famous spring drought of 1893 some 20 places in south-east England, mostly in Kent and Sussex, were rainless for 50 consecutive days or more. One place had an absolute drought of 61 days from March 17 to May 16. In 1938 Nottingham and Ross-on-Wye had a very long partial drought of 100 days from February 1 to May 11. The only year to beat this record was 1893, when at North Ockenden, Romford, only 1.23 inches fell in 128 days, and 1.27 inches at Dungeness in 127 days.

In this general survey of our rainfall we have learnt that rain is heaviest and most frequent in mountainous districts and least over the eastern plains. It is not, however, spread evenly over the year, nor does it follow that the driest month in eastern England is also the driest in the west. Our next step is to discover how monthly rainfall may vary.

Table 1 gives some interesting statistical facts about the ground already covered.

CHAPTER III.

WHAT RAIN CAN DO IN A MONTH

TROPICAL climates are marked by wet and dry seasons. The Mediterranean has dry summers and rainy winters. In Britain, rainfall is spread more evenly through the year, but there are months when the fall is relatively heavier and others when it is comparatively light. Over the lowlands spring is the driest season and autumn the wettest. In mountainous districts it is driest in spring and early summer and wettest in winter.

At Kew, October, with an average of 2.70 inches, is nearly twice as wet as April with 1.45 inches. Seathwaite receives its maximum fall of 16.3 inches in December and has its minimum in June with 6.5 inches. The wettest and driest months are usually six months apart. The dryness of spring is in part due to rising temperature and partly to a falling off in the frequency and intensity of depressions from the Atlantic. In autumn depressions become more frequent and temperature is falling—hence more rain.

Annual rainfall in a particular year may, in exceptional conditions, exceed the average by 70 per cent. or fall below it by 40 or 50 per cent. Much greater variations happen in individual months.

Figure 4 shows how the average rainfall varies from month to month at Kew and Falmouth. In will be observed that Falmouth is much wetter than Kew from October to March, but that from April to September the difference is smaller. Thus the fear of rain need not deter anyone from taking a summer holiday at Falmouth. Kew has a secondary maximum of rainfall in July and August. This is due to thunder rains and not to frequent rain days, and is a feature general in the English lowlands. The falling off in September is due to fewer thunderstorms while at the same time the depression rains of autumn have not set in with all their vigour.

When we examine individual months over a period of a year it is at once patent that great differences from the normal may occur. An exceptionally wet month may have four times the average fall, and an unusually dry one may have no rain at all.

24

In a hundred years the wettest month at Greenwich was 7.6 inches in October, 1880. This is not much more than the average amount for Seathwaite's driest month, June. Anyone who cares to examine rainfall records will discover that it is uncommon for a year to go by without some place in the British Isles experiencing a monthly fall of 25 inches, equal to that of London in twelve months. A month with 25 inches is very difficult to imagine for anyone who has never lived in our wettest areas, because in the English lowlands a fall of five inches in a month would be regarded as very wet.

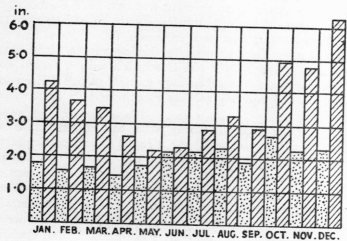

FIG. 4.   MONTHLY RAINFALL AT KEW AND FALMOUTH
(KEW STIPPLED; FALMOUTH SHADED).

This leads to the intriguing question: what is the most rain ever recorded in a single month in Britain? In October, 1909, Llyn Llydaw, Snowdon, at a height of nearly 1,500 feet above sea-level, registered the tremendous quantity of 56.5 inches, or an average of more than 1¾ inches per day, and equal to more than two years' rain in London. On three other occasions a fall of 50 inches has been reached. January, 1872, saw 50.1 inches fall in Borrowdale, and in January, 1928, 50.0 inches was reported from the same place. In March, 1938, Loan, Inverness, received 50 inches, and incredible as it may appear, this same March was one of the driest ever known over much of England. How many people in that dry March, living in the English Lowlands, would have believed that a few hundred miles away as much was falling as they would receive in two years? But remarkable as was this contrast there was an even more astonishing one in Scotland itself. While 50.03 inches was falling at Loan and 40.03 inches at Kinlochquoich, a mere 140 miles away at East Fortune, in East Lothian, a trifle of 0.19 inch was recorded.

Some of the driest months on record are February, 1891; July, 1911; June, 1921; June, 1925; March, 1929; February, 1932, and April, 1938.

In June, 1925, no rain at all was recorded over an area of 6,410 square miles. An interesting event was that both Falmouth and Penzance (where the annual rainfall is over 40 inches) were rainless, whereas Nottingham, with an annual fall of about half these places, has never had an entirely rainless month since records began there in 1867. Nor has Greenwich with a record going back a century ever had an entirely rainless month. Even more amazing was a completely rainless month at rainy Seathwaite in February, 1932.

Although our rainfall varies with the seasons it is well distributed through the year. As a result in any particular year the normal distribution of rain over the months may be quite blotted out by current weather. So great is this factor that it is quite possible in a given year for any month to be the wettest or driest of the year over most of the country. The only areas where this is doubtful are the exceptionally wet ones where the wetness of winter and dryness of spring are more marked than elsewhere. In the wet locality of Borrowdale the rainfall records show that while any month of the year may prove to be the driest, it is very improbable for the wettest month to occur between April and September.

In the Midland city of Nottingham records over 76 years show that July, August and October have each been the wettest month of the year on 13 occasions. At the other end of the scale, January has been the wettest month three times, March twice, and February and April only once each.

Flaming June lived up to its reputation in 1921 when only an area in north-west Scotland had as much as two inches of rain, and England and Wales as a whole had less than one-fifth of the average. June, 1903, was historical for excessive rain in the South Midlands and Thames Valley.

The dreary summer of 1912 brought one of the most tearful

Augusts in meteorological annals. Cornwall and Norfolk experienced more than three times the average rainfall. This was the
month of the great Norfolk rainstorm, which will be described in
the next chapter. After persistently low rainfall during the first
nine months of 1929 excessive rain set in and November was the
wettest for 60 years. Very little of England had less than four
inches of rain, while most of Wales, Devon and Cornwall had more
than ten inches. Falmouth totalled 13.4 inches, Plymouth 12.2
inches, Tavistock 17.9 inches, and at Princetown, on Dartmoor, the
great downfall of 29.4 inches occurred.

Over England and Wales, May, 1932, was the wettest for 160
years. Severe flooding scourged the Don Valley at Bentley, Yorkshire, and at Nottingham part of the residential suburb of West
Bridgford was under a considerable depth of water.

October, 1939, cannot be ignored here on account of the very
heavy rain which fell in Kent. By a sharp reversal of normal
conditions Kent was wetter than either Snowdonia or the Lake
District, a number of places exceeding 10 inches. Margate totalled
10.28 inches, an inch more than fell there in the whole of 1921!
Our versatile climate can, therefore, in Kent at least, produce as
much rain in a very wet month as may fall in a very dry year.
Dover, in that same October, had 13.88 inches, and Folkestone
14.11 inches, amounts more suited to Borrowdale than to one of
the dry counties of England.

Although we have an accurate knowledge of rainfall averages
we are only too conscious that when we peer into the next twelve
months they are almost useless as a guide as to what may happen
in any particular month. Wet months and dry months alike cast
no shadow before them to warn us of their approach.

CHAPTER IV.

SOME DAYS BRING DELUGES

EVERYONE knows the persistent splash of a wet day, but few could say how much falls in these visitations. Guesses would probably be very wide of the mark. On a wet day some time ago the writer remarked to a friend that 0.9 inch of rain had fallen, to receive the reply, "I was out in it, and would not have been surprised if you had said five inches." This remark is interesting and typical. To many people the mention of rainfall amount is meaningless. It is very unlikely that the speaker had ever experienced five inches in a day; nor has the writer. We all know what a pound of sugar is, or a ton of coal, but an inch of rain is another matter. Before we can understand we need a "yard-stick."

With annual rainfall we adopted 25 inches per annum, London's fall, as a guide. In the same way let us bear in mind that two inches is an average month's fall in the English lowlands. In the lowlands, too, a quarter of an inch in a day is a respectable fall, half an inch is not common, and an inch or more of rain in one day would ordinarily occur only once or twice in a year. The rainfall at Nottingham was analysed over a period of twenty years. It was found that on an average 284 days in a year have less than one-tenth of an inch of rain, 46 days have from 0.10 inch to 0.25 inch, 24 days from 0.25 inch to 0.50 inch, 9 days from 0.50 inch to 1.00 inch, and only 2 days with over one inch. On an average the wettest day of the year is 1.27 inches, compared with 1.24 inches at Greenwich, 1.26 inches at Aberdeen, 1.46 inches at Southampton, 1.50 inches at Buxton, 1.61 inches at Falmouth and 1.73 inches at Valentia, Ireland. These facts give us our "yard-stick."

The official records of rainfall in Britain contain numerous instances of more rain falling in a single day than one would expect in a month. The rest of this chapter comments on some of the more sensational occurrences of this character.

One of the most disastrous floods of this century happened at the little town of Louth, in Lincolnshire, on May 29, 1920. This was a local depression rain resulting from the meeting of two moist currents, one from the south-east and the other from the south-west. The low hills of the Lincolnshire Wolds had the full fury of the rain with 4.69 inches in three hours at Elkington Hall, and 3.95 inches at Horncastle. Louth itself recorded the comparatively modest total of 1.42 inches. The flood water (something like five million tons fell over 22 square miles) cut through Louth, drowning 22 persons and causing something like £100,000 worth of damage. It is thought that the flood water was dammed by débris, and the bursting of this obstruction released the raging torrent. Fortunately, our great rainstorms are rarely associated with loss of life like this.

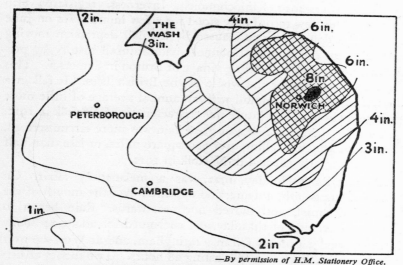

—*By permission of H.M. Stationery Office.*

FIG. 5. THE GREAT NORFOLK RAINSTORM OF AUG. 25-26, 1912
(FROM BRITISH RAINFALL, 1912).

One of the most remarkable rainstorms on record in our islands deluged Norfolk on August 26, 1912. A small but well-developed depression off the Kent coast that morning moved slowly northwards to be off Cromer in the evening. An intense rainstorm resulted, giving more than 3 inches over 3,463 square miles. Of this area 1,039 square miles had more than five inches. The map of this rain shown in Figure 5 reveals the maximum fall focused a little to the east of Norwich, where Brundall recorded 8.09 inches, an average four month's total! Norwich itself experienced 7.3 inches, over a quarter of the annual average. With such a visitation flooding was inevitably serious. On a wall in the city of Norwich is a tablet which records the high water mark of all the severe floods of the past 300 years. The highest of these floods bore the date 1614, but the vast flood of 1912 went as much as 15 inches higher. The damage to roads and bridges in the county of Norfolk alone was about £28,000. A large area of land remained under water throughout the following winter. It is fortunate that the local configuration of the land offered no steep slope to accelerate the rush of flood water.

On November 12, 1897, Seathwaite had 8.03 inches of rain. This constituted a British record for one day for some years, but on October 11, 1916, Kinlochquoich, Inverness, registered 8.20 inches. This new record only stood for a few months, for on June 28, 1917, a deluge of rain, caused by a small depression moving eastwards up the English Channel, made rainfall history by producing 9.56 inches at the little village of Bruton in Somerset. This record still stands for the whole of the British Isles. It fell in a district of moderate rainfall with an annual average of little more than 30 inches. This feature was characteristic of Norfolk in 1912. In the 1917 deluge the area of great rain was more circumscribed, more than 4 inches falling over 800 square miles, or less than half the area similarly affected in Norfolk in 1912.

August Bank Holiday, 1922, was a melancholy affair. On Sunday, August 6th, a depression appeared over the mouth of the English Channel, and moved north-eastwards. Rain began to fall in the evening of that day and continued for about 24 hours. In this period 3.4 inches fell in Nottingham, and at Worksop over 5 inches came down in a fall lasting 28 hours. Two inches of this fell in three hours on Bank Holiday. This was the first occasion that as much as 4 inches had fallen in a day in Nottinghamshire. Over two inches fell in a belt of country from Hampshire to West Yorkshire.

November, 1929, will be remembered for the severe floods in the Rhondda Valley on the 11th, when 8.31 inches was measured at Lluest Wen Reservoir. This is the largest fall recorded in one day in Wales, but it must be remembered that in the very wet Snowdon district a number of gauges are not read each day and so heavier falls may have been missed.

Dwellers in the Esk Valley in the North Riding of Yorkshire had an unpleasant experience in July, 1930, which will always find a noteworthy place in rainfall history. Heavy rain fell on four successive days with its peak on July 22nd. On that day 5.70 inches fell at Castleton and 5.20 inches at Danby. In four days Castleton had the remarkable total of 11.97 inches and Danby 11.73 inches. Eight other gauges in the neighbourhood reported from 8 to 11 inches. The annual fall of these places is only 31 to 36 inches, so that four months' normal precipitation came down in four days. An unprecedented feature was the use of the Whitby lifeboat at Ruswarp, two miles inland, where it was launched on the floods and used to rescue trapped people.

The town of Boston, Lincolnshire, near the junction of the River Witham with the Wash, has a placid existence, and like all fen localities a low rainfall of 23 inches a year. Until 1931 the most sensational event in Boston's rainfall chronicle had been a fall of 3.10 inches on September 29, 1883, on which day Skegness recorded 4.31 inches. On the morning of August 8, 1931, however, a great rainstorm broke, giving the sensational amount of 6.10 inches, of which 4 inches fell in about two hours. This was over a quarter of a year's supply. One would have supposed that after such a phenomenal fall the chances were that a long sequence of years would elapse before anything like this happened again. It does not do to rely too much on "probabilities" in rainfall, for only six years later on July 15, 1937, 5.46 inches of rain splashed down in twelve hours at Boston. On August 12, 1948, the Tweed Valley experienced the greatest deluge ever recorded in that district. The focus of the rain was at Kelso, Roxburgh, where 6.21 inches fell. Severe floods and great damage ensued, several bridges were washed away, and the River Tweed at Kelso rose 6½ inches higher than in the previous highest floods of 1831.

Let us leave the mainland and cross to the Isle of Man. This mountainous island has a climate which does not favour heavy thunder rains, as we shall see later. Its heavy rains are of the depression type, but its annual rainfall is not nearly so heavy as that of the Lake District, Snowdonia or Dartmoor. Up to 1918 the heaviest day's fall in the island was 3.82 inches at the Dhoon on November 6, 1890. A great rain on September 15, 1918, produced a new record when 4.95 inches fell at Douglas. At Ramsey 3.37 inches was reported on December 20, 1929, but this record was broken when a sweeping rain on September 17, 1930, brought 4.35 inches. No loss of life occurred, but damage to property and livestock was extensive. Wreckage brought down by the Sulby River was strewn on the beach at Ramsey as well as carried some distance out to sea. The railway line linking Ramsey with Douglas was unusable for several days.

This glance at some of our great rains is far from complete, but shows what severe visitations may from time to time disturb the relative placidity of our climate, even in dry districts.

Most of the heavy rains described were depression rains. The most "intense" rains in Britain accompany thunderstorms. As these rains do not, as a rule, last very long the rainfall totals do not always seem so impressive. It is the *rate* of fall which makes thunder-rains so awe-inspiring, and they deserve a new chapter.

LIGHTNING IN A JUNE THUNDERSTORM AT BEXLEY, KENT.

CHAPTER V.

THUNDERSTORMS—OUR WEATHER IN A TEMPER

THUNDERSTORMS are the most spectacular and awe-inspiring items on our weather programme. The piling-up of a dark majestic thundercloud on a summer day, with the warm sultry air hushed as though waiting and listening, has all the making of effective drama. So, too, has the snapping of the tension with the dazzling flash, the rolling echoes of the thunder, and the furious rain when the storm breaks.

What causes thunderstorms? One thinks of the cynic's description of an English summer—three fine days and a thunderstorm. It is true to say that heat is one of the causes of thunderstorms, but that in itself will not produce them. There are long spells of intense heat in the Sahara Desert without any storm. It is necessary for heat to be allied to moisture. The torrential character of thunder rains indicates a large supply of moisture to give them birth. Our weather is not like a conjurer; it cannot produce heavy rain out of an empty hat.

When the sun beats down on the earth's surface the air gets very warm, expands and rises. This process is most in evidence on a warm afternoon. If the barometer is high and the air dry, probably nothing more will happen than the formation of those sharply-defined white cumulus clouds which look like masses of cotton-wool. These towering clouds are formed by the moisture condensing as the ascending warm currents become cooled. Incidentally, these conditions favour gliding, and a glider will find himself soaring upwards at considerable speed under a cumulus cloud. It also explains why some summer days which appear perfect for flying are "bumpy." As the afternoon passes into evening the sun loses its strength, the ascending warm currents fail and the cumulus clouds die from lack of nourishment.

A cumulus cloud is in essence the embryo of a thunderstorm. It may develop into a storm or not, according as to whether the air is sufficiently moist or too dry. A storm produced in this way may be called a summer heat thunderstorm and is most likely to occur in the afternoon or early evening. It is not likely to be very heavy and does not often occur when the barometer is high.

Something more is needed to cause a severe storm. That something is what is known as a large temperature lapse-rate. The

C

lapse-rate is simply the rate of fall in temperature as one ascends from the earth's surface. Let us leave rainfall for the moment and consider temperature. The normal fall in temperature is about 3°F. for every 1,000 feet of ascent. When this lapse-rate exists the air is said to be stable, because each layer of air at stated heights is at its natural temperature relative to layers above and below. In other words, the lower air has no tendency to rise, and the higher layers no tendency to sink. If, however, the lapse-rate is considerably in excess of 3°F. per thousand feet—that is, the temperature falls more quickly than it should as we ascend—then the air is unstable. Visualise this by imagining a very cold layer of air above the warm surface layer. A condition of top-heaviness is in being. The heavy cold air tries to sink and the warm light air rises, just as a cork held at the bottom of a tank of water will rise if released. If it is a warm summer afternoon the surface air will move rapidly upwards to great heights and if it contains much moisture this will be condensed as heavy rain. Just how this process develops such enormous electrical tension as to cause the spark or discharge we call lightning has not been satisfactorily explained, but research is continually proceeding.

Our heaviest thunderstorms occur in the summer months, because only when the air is warm can it contain sufficient moisture to form a potential reservoir for these torrential down-pours. For the same reason thunder occurs most frequently in summer in those parts of England where temperature is highest. England has few thunderstorms in winter, but they occur more frequently at that season on our western seaboard, which has few storms in summer. The thunderstorms in winter are different in type from those of summer. They result from cold polar winds blowing over relatively warm sea water. This makes the surface air too warm relatively to the air at higher levels, and so produces the instability necessary for thunder.

The air before a storm is frequently associated with a sensation of heaviness—it is sultry—out of proportion to the temperature. It is sometimes said that thunderstorms cool and freshen the atmosphere. The downpour of rain invariably lowers the thermometer, especially on a very hot day. The rain however quickly raises the humidity, causing a clammy warmth. If the rainfall is not great and the storm a short one the atmosphere may become more stifling after the storm than before. When storms occur in sluggish areas of low barometer this increase in discomfort is common. No! thunderstorms, as such, do not freshen the atmosphere. When, however, a storm is associated with what is called a "cold front" then a cool fresh air will arrive. It is this phenomenon which has given rise to the popular belief that storms freshen the air. The truth is that it is the arrival of the cold front which brings the freshness, and this happens even if no storm occurs.

An excellent example of this was given at Nottingham on June 6, 1942. After four days of brilliantly fine hot weather with the thermometer soaring to 85°F. in the screen the author noticed a reading of 84°F. at 5 p.m. with low humidity. In the evening thundery clouds appeared in the south-west. At 8 p.m. the temperature was 78°F. and the air had become oppressively still. At 8.30 p.m. there were rumbles of thunder but no rain. Half an

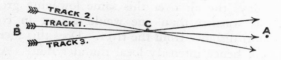

FIG. 6.   PATHS OF THUNDERSTORMS.

hour later the temperature was still high at 77°F., and the barometer, which in the morning had been 30.2 inch, had fallen to 30.0 inch. About 9.30 p.m. a breeze sprang up from the west and the temperature dropped several degrees. By 10 p.m. it was 70°F. and felt cool and fresh; the barometer was now rising again. An hour later a strong westerly wind was blowing with the thermometer at 65°F., which felt cold compared with the sultry air of a few hours before. This sequence of weather shows the passage of a cold front after great heat. It produced a thunder cloud, a little thunder, but no storm. The following day, although sunshine was continuous, the thermometer never rose above 65°F., and people erroneously remarked that the thunder had "cleared the air."

In some places thunderstorms are thought to follow certain paths, such as the course of a river. The author found that in a small town in Yorkshire a belief existed that the river affected the storms so that they passed to one side or the other of the town. This is highly improbable, and the explanation is doubtless to be found in the optical illusion caused by perspective.

In Figure 6 an observer at point A is assumed to be looking

towards point B. A thunderstorm moving along track 1 would pass directly over A. Thunderstorms following tracks 2 and 3 would also appear to be approaching A, and when they came close, point C, their true paths would reveal themselves. The observer at A if unacquainted with the effects of perspective would assume they had swerved to left and right of him.

It is quite possible that high hills will affect thunderstorm paths, but it is an open question whether small hills and valleys can do so. At Nottingham there exists the belief that storms tend to follow the valley of the River Trent. In order to test this idea the author collected data from 34 rain-gauges in and round Nottingham for 135 thunderstorms covering ten years. The results showed that on the whole thunder rains were heavier on low-lying ground near the river, but further research should be made on similar lines in other parts of the country. It is known that on hot summer days the air over this same low-lying ground near Nottingham is warmer than one would expect in comparison with that a short distance from the river. Does this increase local convection, and hence intensify local thunder rain? As yet this is speculation.

As has been stated, the warmest areas in summer have most thunder, and storms are less frequent in the cooler north and west.

The following list gives the average number of days with thunder in a year at various places.

Days with
Thunder
per annum

20	Wakefield
19	Huddersfield and Norwich
18	Stonyhurst and Cranwell
17	Felixstowe
16	Hull and Cromer
15	Shoeburyness
14	Kew and Cambridge
13	Cheltenham, Southport, Spurn Head, Tunbridge Wells.
12	Bath, Folkestone, Nottingham, Manchester, Margate, Sheffield, York
11	Dungeness, Harrogate, Oxford, Southampton, Skegness, Yarmouth
10	Buxton, Eastbourne
9	Brighton, Cardiff, Dover, Douglas, Durham, Guernsey, Liverpool, Torquay
8	Dublin, Oban, Scarborough, Ventnor
7	Dundee, Glasgow, Jersey, Llandudno, Newquay, Orkneys, Portland Bill, Paisley, Rothesay, Tynemouth, Valentia
6	Bournemouth, Aberystwyth, Aberdeen, Holyhead, Scilly Isles.
5	Birr Castle, Armagh, Falmouth, Leith, Malin Head, Plymouth, Roches Point
4	Donaghadee, Ilfracombe, Wick
3	St. Ann's Head, Stornoway.
1	Lerwick

The most thundery place in the world, so far as is known, is Buitenzorg, Java, where thunder occurs on 322 days a year.

The number of thunderstorms which occur all over the world is very great. Dr. C. E. P. Brooks, in his memoir on the distribution of thunderstorms, after collecting data from over 3,000 places, estimates that the enormous number of 44,000 storms occur a day. Assuming an average duration of one hour, there must be something like 1,800 storms in progress somewhere in the world at any given moment.

Sailors say that lightning runs along the decks of ships, but from experience at sea the author, having seen the phenomenon, believes it is nothing more than reflection of the lightning on the wet steel decks.

Some people are nervous about thunderstorms, and in some cases this fear is so great that a person may relapse into a state of terror. Some will cower in dark places, presumably because if they fail to see the lightning they may persuade themselves it is not there. Others cover mirrors, saying they attract lightning. It is difficult to say what causes this form of neurosis. Few people have been so close to a lightning flash as to receive injuries. In all probability very few of these nervous people have ever been near to danger. Few deaths from lightning occur in our islands, perhaps a yearly average of fifteen or so. Death from lightning is thus a remote possibility. A nervous person will say, "Yes, but it might be me." The same person, however, having an opportunity of one in three millions of winning a sweepstake would not think much of his chances. Nervous people gain confidence, and are even cured sometimes, by being in the company of those who show indifference to possible danger in a storm.

It is sometimes said that motor-cars are very safe in a storm owing to insulation formed by their rubber tyres. This hypothesis is a poor one, as the moment that the tyres and the road surface become wet with rain the insulation ceases. If motor-cars possess some safety it is probably due to a "Faraday Cage" effect of their metal work.

Do not shelter under a tree in a storm, and do not touch wire-fencing. If at home, earth your radio to protect it from possible damage.

Having taken these simple precautions remember that a thunderstorm is a most wonderful sight. Do, please, enjoy it. If you are sufficiently interested to make notes about the storms that visit your locality, Mr. S. Morris Bower, of the Thunderstorm Census, Oakes, Huddersfield, would be glad to receive your reports.

The most remarkable display of lightning seen by the author was at Skegness, Lincolnshire, on July 12, 1912. It commenced at 8.30 p.m. and lasted till 1 a.m. on the 13th. The greatest frequency was reached from 9 p.m. to 10 p.m., when 700 flashes were counted. In all, about 1,400 flashes were visible. Only a few drops of rain fell. This followed a hot day with the temperature reaching 91 in London and 86 at Lincoln.

This exhibition of natural fireworks was beaten in the storm which broke over London on July 9-10, 1923. In six hours the astonishing number of 6,924 flashes of lightning were recorded. The most in one hour was 1,540, or 26 flashes a minute. The main rainfall in this storm stretched in a narrow belt from the coast of Sussex to Grantham, Lincolnshire, in which a large area had over 3 inches of rain. The largest falls were 4.55 inches at Rottingdean, and 4.04 inches at Newhaven. Near Brighton 2.96 inches was registered and in the London district 2.56 inches at Hampstead.

Towards the end of August, 1930, after a rather poor summer, a hot spell arrived of unusual intensity for so late in the season. The thermometer touched 94 in London and 92 at Attenborough, Notts., on three successive days. August 29th was a most oppressive day with a high humidity. In the evening a violent thunderstorm broke over Nottingham with large hailstones. Figure 7 shows the distribution of rainfall in this storm round Nottingham, and gives an excellent example of how large differences can occur over short distances. Nearly two inches fell near the centre of the storm, but hardly any four miles to the north-west.

On June 16, 1917, a heavy thunderstorm brought to London the greatest day's rain ever measured in the metropolis. More than four inches fell over about half a square mile in the Campden Hill neighbourhood. The maximum fall observed was 4.65 inches in about 2½ hours. Kensington Gardens received 3.65 inches. Strangely enough in this storm no rain fell in London south-east of a line drawn from West Ham through Liverpool Street to Wimbledon. If the rate of fall at Campden Hill could have been maintained it would have meant a year's rain for London in 13 hours.

A storm at Cranwell, Lincs., on July 11, 1932, brought rain of a

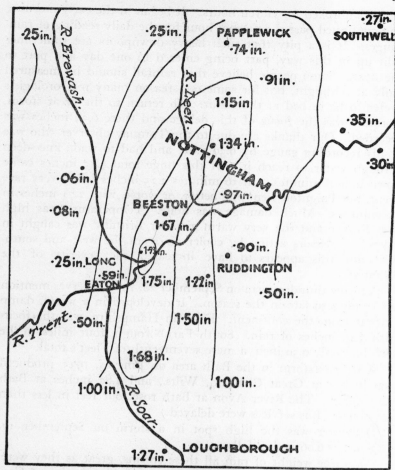

·25 in.

R. Erewash.

·25 in.

PAPPLEWICK
·74 in.

·27 in.
SOUTHWELL

·91 in.

R. Leen.

·35 in.

1·15 in.

·30 in.

NOTTINGHAM

· 1·34 in.

·06 in.

·97 in.

·08 in.

BEESTON

1·67 in.

·25 in. LONG

1·73 in.

·90 in.

RUDDINGTON

·59 in.

EATON

1·75 in.   1·22 in.

·50 in.

R. Trent. ·50 in.

1·50 in.

1·68 in.

1·00 in.

R. Soar.

1·00 in.

LOUGHBOROUGH

1·27 in.

FIG. 7.   RAINFALL DISTRIBUTION ROUND NOTTINGHAM DURING
THUNDERSTORM OF AUGUST 29, 1930.

very rare intensity.   The total fall for the day was 5.14 inches, and
of this 4.98 inches fell in 120 minutes.   Such a large amount in
two hours is probably unprecedented in British rainfall records.

Those who live in Devon and Cornwall, or who were visiting
those delightful counties on August 4, 1938, will long remember
it, for there broke a thunderstorm which made a landmark in the
meteorological history of south-west England for severity, duration
and area.   Over a considerable part of both counties it lasted

almost unbroken for eleven hours.   It began in the early morning
and continued past the normal hour for the daily reading of rain-
gauges.   It is a pity that such heavy downpours are sometimes
split up in this way, part being entered to one day and part to
the next.   Some people believe that rainfall should be measured
daily at midnight, but for some odd reason many meteorologists
prefer to be in bed at that hour.   To return to the great storm,
Torquay was the focus of this deluge and there 6.39 inches was
recorded.   Our thanks are due to the Torquay observer who was
at his recording gauge by 6.30 a.m., and had to wade knee-deep
through water to reach it.   Of this huge total 4.25 inches came
down in 108 minutes.   In 56 minutes 2.25 inches fell, a very rare
event, but Paignton went one better, or worse, with 2.71 inches in
45 minutes.   Much damage was done.   Temperature was high
over France and the very warm air over Brittany was caught in
a kind of scissors action by cooler air from the west and south-
west, and this appears to have increased the severity of the
visitation.

A heavy thunderstorm on September 26, 1933, deserves mention
for coming so late in the season.   It developed in a warm, damp
current from the continent.   Fleet, in Hampshire, was the focus
with 5.16 inches of rain.   South Farnborough, four miles to the
east, had only 0.30 inch, a mere seventeenth of Fleet's total.

A thunderstorm in the Bath area on June 25, 1935, produced
5.00 inches at Great Chalfield, Wilts., and 4.83 inches at Bath
waterworks.   The River Avon at Bath rose four feet in less than
two hours.   Bus services were delayed.

Doncaster was the high spot in a storm on September 17,
1913, when 6.06 inches fell.

For sheer weight of rain all these storms, great as they were,
must take a secondary place to the tremendous visitation at Cannington on August 18, 1924.   A westerly air current of polar
origin was blowing over southern England, causing unstable conditions.   There was nothing to presage the torrential downpour
which burst over Somerset.   The rain is described as coming down
in solid sheets as though being emptied out of buckets.   The
noise of the rain almost drowned the thunder.   At Brymore
House, Cannington, the gauge showed 9.40 inches of rain,
of which about 8 inches fell in five hours, possibly without rival in
our records.   The intensity of the rain exceeded that of the Louth
floods, but fortunately geographical configuration was such that no

great rush of flood water passed through a town. Normally, Cannington experiences 31 inches a year, so that this fall was nearly a third of the annual average.

When we read of such phenomenal falls there is a danger that we may lose our perspective. It is well, therefore, to recall that two inches of rain a *month* is typical of lowland England and that only about 35 days a year reach or exceed a quarter of an inch.

So far, in considering heavy thunder rains we have dealt with great amounts. There is another type of storm in which rain cascades down with terrific intensity for a brief period, and such storms are more frequent. In such cases the short duration of the rain prevents the recording of large totals. It has just been pointed out that in the Cannington storm 8 inches fell in five hours, which gives a rate of 1.6 inches per hour. While this was phenomenal for so long a time it would not be a remarkable rate over a short period.

The author once recorded 0.49 inch in eight minutes, a rate of 3.67 inches an hour, and on two other occasions noted a fall of an inch in 15 minutes, on September 3, 1916, and September, 1931.

On July 22, 1880, 2.90 inches fell at Cowbridge in Glamorgan in 30 minutes, or 5.80 inches per hour. Please note that although this rate was maintained for half an hour, there is no case on record of 5.80 inches falling in an hour. The largest amount ever recorded in a single hour in the British Isles was a fall of 3.63 inches at Maidenhead on July 12, 1901. The ferocity of short falls is such that, in homely language, the pace kills. The shorter the time the greater the possible intensity, just as a hundred yards race can be run at a much greater speed than a half mile.

At Canterbury on August 7, 1875, 2.12 inches of rain fell in 20 minutes, or 6.36 inches per hour. Guernsey, on August 14, 1914, recorded 1.50 inches in 15 minutes. The most extraordinary case of intense rain of which we have any record was at Preston on August 10, 1893, when in the short space of five minutes 1.25 inches of rain are said to have fallen, giving the enormous rate of 15.00 inches per hour, which rate if sustained would produce a year's rain for London in little more than an hour and a half.

The world's record for rainfall intensity appears to be held by Porto Bello, Panama, where 2.47 inches were once registered in three minutes, and at Opid's Camp, San Gabriel Range, California, when, in April, 1926, as much as 1.02 inches fell in one minute, the latter being a rate of 61 inches an hour. We may note in passing that Baguio, Philippine Islands, recorded 46.0 inches in 24 hours in June, 1911.

It will be understood that a very incomplete picture has been given of our great storms, but these examples serve to show what may happen. At such times the lowlands can show downpours in a day equal to anything ever recorded in our wettest mountain districts, but they cannot compete with wet areas in sustained rain. Twenty inches have been known to fall in seven days in our mountains.

Hail

When hail falls it is usually associated with thundery conditions. Hailstones are frozen raindrops. When a super-cooled waterdrop impinges on a snow crystal it solidifies. A falling hailstone may be caught in an ascending current and carried upwards again. This process may be continued several times and each time a fresh layer of ice is formed on the stone. Eventually it becomes large enough to fall to the ground. At times hailstones can reach a great size. On September 3, 1916, hailstones measuring an inch and a quarter in diameter fell at Nottingham. During a severe thunderstorm on July 22, 1925, stones were reported at Woolwich and Plumstead as large as a man's fist and weighing 8 ounces. Heavy hail occurred at the break-up of the heat-wave in August, 1930. Stones 1½ inches in diameter fell at Peebles on August 29th and 1,200 panes of glass were reported to have been broken in one hotel alone.

On August 12, 1938, hail lay deep on the ground at Wold Newton, near Bridlington, and remained till next day. It was described as "deep snow in August." Apparently some people are unaware that deep snow does not fall in the English Lowlands in that month.

An amazing hailstorm broke about 4 a.m. on September 22, 1935, over parts of Northamptonshire. At Great Billing evidence was obtained of the great size of the stones from the condition of asbestos forming the roof of a garage. In one of the apertures it was possible to draw a circle four inches in diameter. It will probably astonish most people that hailstones of this size can fall in Britain. Few persons have ever seen a hailstone here as much as two inches across. In all probability the hailstones of this storm have never been exceeded in size in this country.

Tornadoes

A tornado may be regarded as a small but very intense depression. Its diameter may be only a few feet or as much as a mile. Its life is a brief but destructive one. In England tornadoes are unusual events, but they do develop sometimes, and are associated with thundery conditions. On a hot day small rotating whirls of dust are sometimes seen on roads. These are embryonic tornadoes, and nearly all die in this pre-natal state.

On July 7, 1938, a tornado occurred in the Chiltern Hills, coincident with the passage of a "cold front." It formed in open hilly country a mile or two north of Boxmoor, Hertfordshire. The track was about 100 yards wide and extended 8½ miles from its origin. Near Boxmoor a stationary motor-cycle and sidecar was blown diagonally across the road. The track resembled a battlefield, with hundreds of trees felled and haystacks torn apart.

A severe thunderstorm broke over Birmingham at 2.30 p.m. G.M.T. on Sunday, June 14, 1931, and about the same time a tornado appeared in the Sparkhill district. It travelled rapidly along a track varying in width from 200 to 800 yards, passing through Greet, Small Heath and Bordesley, to the Erdington boundary of the city. A scar ten or twelve miles long was torn in the face of Birmingham. Much damage was done, houses smashed, roofs stripped, windows blown inwards and trees uprooted. One death was caused. The duration of the tornado at any spot was about two minutes.

Aurora

Though not connected with thunderstorms, the aurora is an electro-magnetic phenomenon, so a word may be said about it here. It is not often seen in the south of England, but in the north of Scotland it is, comparatively, a common sight. This electrical discharge takes place most frequently 50 to 70 miles above the earth's surface.

An examination of the *Monthly Weather Reports* of the Meteorological Office over a period of ten years shows that somewhere in Scotland it will be seen on an average on 70 nights a year. In 1938 it was reported on about 120 nights. Sometimes it will be observed on as many as 15 nights or more in a single month.

A most magnificent display of the aurora was observed over the British Isles on the evening of January 25, 1938, continuing into the early hours of the 26th. It was accompanied by a great

magnetic storm. This brilliant aurora was seen as far south as
the Mediterranean. Red and green were the dominant colours.

This chapter on torrential rains may be aptly closed by saying
that there is evidence that on rare occasions there are local downpours over very small areas of a devastating fury beyond anything
which has been recorded by any rain-gauge.

In the north of England, where the four counties of Yorkshire, Durham, Westmorland and Cumberland cluster to a
point, there is the most extensive mass of high land south of the
Tweed. In this district, on Stainmore, on the border of Yorkshire and Westmorland, at a height of 1,500 feet there occurred on
June 18, 1930, cloudbursts of such violence that five great scars
were torn in the surface of the ground. One scar was 150 yards
long by 50 yards wide, and had been scooped out to a depth of
from four to nine feet. The question arises—how many inches
of rain were represented by such a mass of water falling from a
height? The only close eye-witness, a gamekeeper, described it
as like a solid fall of water covering the hillside like a sheet. But
nobody was very near these cloudbursts, and had they been it is
doubtful if they would have survived to tell the tale.

A similar event happened in the Driffield district of East
Yorkshire in a field near Langtoft on July 3, 1892. The water is
described as roaring like the sea, and the famous meteorologist
Symons expressed the opinion that over the small area concerned
100 inches might possibly have fallen! This would represent
three years of normal rain for the locality. Though there are
5,000 rain-gauges in use in these islands, they are not very thick
on the ground. One may walk all day and never see one, so that
the chances of a gauge being on the spot when one of these rare
cloudbursts materialises is remote. Perhaps that does not much
matter, as no gauge yet designed could cope with such an attack.

An old lady once remarked, "I can understand how you
measure the rain where the gauge is, but what puzzles me is how
you measure it on the ground where the gauge isn't."

In cloudbursts such as those mentioned this remark loses its
apparent absurdity.

CHAPTER VI.

Britain's Warm and Cold Spots

Is it warm or cold? The answer affects our comfort, our prosperity and our mentality. If the weather is too warm we become lazy; a cooler atmosphere makes us more alert. There is one great difference between temperature and rainfall. Rain falls over the English Lowlands for only about five per cent. of the time, but temperature is with us every hour of the day and night, varying continuously.

When a meteorologist talks of temperature he is invariably referring to the temperature of the air. The air is cool in the early morning and warmer in the afternoon, a daily event governed by the rising and setting of the sun, though other factors also exert an influence.

How does the sun warm the air? This is not by any means as simple as it seems. The air is not warmed by the sun's rays shining through it. If that were so it would be warm on mountain tops and snow would not lie there as it does. One is apt to think of the sun as a super-furnace radiating heat like one's fireside. A more correct view would be to regard it as a transmitting station radiating waves of electric energy through space. Part of this energy reaches us as light, part is converted into heat on reaching the earth's surface. The sun's rays warm the ground and the ground warms the air by contact and convection. A little heat also reaches the air from the warming of the minute particles of dust it contains.

Temperature is measured by a thermometer, but whereas the measurement of rain is a relatively simple matter, it is much more difficult to get an accurate air temperature. If ten different people in a road were each given a thermometer and asked to place it in the shade and read it at a fixed time, the result would probably be ten different temperature readings. So many things may cause an error, such as reflection of the sun from the ground or from clouds, or radiation from a neighbouring wall or building.

To prevent this and obtain comparable temperature readings, meteorologists mount their thermometers in a standard screen, which is designed to allow a free passage of air but prevents other

45

factors from vitiating the result. This is called a Stevenson Screen, and the thermometers are mounted so as to be about four feet above the ground. A smaller screen has been designed more recently by Mr. E. G. Bilham, A.R.C.Sc., B.Sc., of the Meteorological Office.

Two thermometers are mounted in the screen, a maximum for reading the highest temperature and one for recording the minimum. As a rule, both thermometers are read at 9 a.m. G.M.T. The maximum reading is entered to the previous day and the

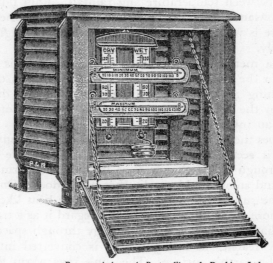

—By permission of Pastorelli and Rapkin, Ltd.

FIG. 8.   STEVENSON'S THERMOMETER SCREEN.

minimum to the present day; that is, the maximum read at 9 a.m. on, say, May 10th, is entered to May 9th, and the minimum to May 10th. The maximum thermometer is re-set by shaking down the mercury, as in a doctor's clinical thermometer, and the minimum by tilting it to allow the index to slide to the end of the spirit column farther from the bulb.

Temperature is recorded in this way every day. At the end of the month all the maximum readings are totalled and divided by the number of days in the month. This gives the mean maximum temperature for the month. By treating the minimum readings in the same way the mean minimum is obtained. The mean temperature of the month is a point half way between the mean maximum and the mean minimum. If the mean temperatures for each month of the year are added together and the total divided by twelve, this gives the mean annual temperature for the year concerned. When readings have been made regularly over a long period, say 20 or 30 years, then it is possible to work out *average* values for each month and for the year.

Temperature is varying all the time, from day to day and hour to hour, and the mean temperature of a month or year is the point about which all the fluctuations balance.

In order to get a clear picture of how the temperature is varying over the country on any day or month, one must draw maps showing the distribution. How this is done is shown in Figure 9. On this map temperatures vary from 54°F. in the top left-hand corner to 72°F. towards the bottom right-hand corner.

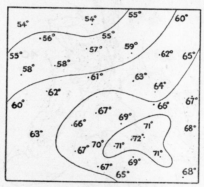

FIG. 9.   HOW A TEMPERATURE
MAP IS MADE.

The lines are isotherms, or lines of equal temperature. They are drawn for 55°F., 60°F., 65°F. and 70°F.

Figures 10 to 15 show the mean temperature, the mean maximum and the mean minimum temperatures for the two months of January and July over the British Isles. They are worth careful study. The reader might like to decide which are the warmest and coldest parts of the British Isles in January and July. A rather more difficult test is to try and arrange the following eight places in order of mean temperature in (a) January, (b) July: Aberdeen, Bournemouth, Buxton, Cambridge, Kew, Llandudno, Rothesay and the Scilly Isles. The correct order will be given later in the chapter.

Many people have what may be called a north-south complex
regarding temperature.   They believe that if A is further south
than B then it must be warmer.   This point of view is a perfectly
natural one.   It is hot at the equator and cold at the poles.
Nigeria is warmer than Spain; Spain is warmer than Britain, and
Britain is warmer than Norway.   It is not, however, always true
that if a place is further south than another it is necessarily
warmer.   Geographical factors, such as the distribution of sea
and land, may have such a decisive effect that they may over-ride

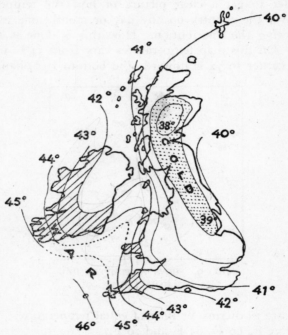

FIG. 10.   MEAN TEMPERATURE IN JANUARY.

the effect of latitude.   The shape and position of the British Isles
upsets some of our north-south ideas.   In Figure 10 the January
isotherm of 41°F. runs from the Hebrides to Wales, then to
Southampton where it turns eastwards, skirting the south coast
to Kent.   Thus Lewis, in the Hebrides, has a similar January
temperature to the eastern half of the south coast of England.
If temperature fell regularly from south to north the isotherms,
or temperature lines, on the map for January would run from

east to west. It would be more correct to say that temperature in January was highest in the south-west and fell towards the north-east.

In summer, Fig. 11, conditions more closely resemble the popular idea of temperature distribution, but even here there are marked divergencies. The south coast is not the hottest part of England in summer, as might be supposed. The July heat focus is round London and the Thames Valley. Cornwall is similar to Yorkshire. The city of York has the same mean July tempera-

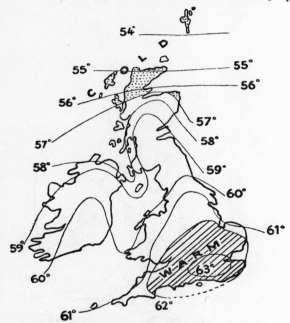

FIG 11. MEAN TEMPERATURE IN JULY.

ture as the Scilly Isles, 61°F. The other four maps, Figures 12 to 15, showing day and night values, should be studied along with Figures 10 and 11.

Observe the isotherm of 42°F. in Figure 10. It comes down from near the Hebrides, forms a loop over north-east Ireland, turns north again over the Irish Sea to touch the Isle of Man, then swings south once more through west Wales into Devon. Here it swerves abruptly east to skirt the Isle of Wight. What is the cause of this wandering path? Not mere chance, for there is

D

nothing irrational about climate. In our opening chapter we saw
how great is the influence of the Atlantic.

In winter the British Isles are washed by relatively warm water,
which has a higher specific heat than the land surface. In
January, therefore, the land cools more quickly than the sea, and
the temperature of the air over the sea and over coastal districts
is determined largely by that of the water. Apply this fact to
Figure 10 and isotherm 42°F. The loop over Ireland is due to

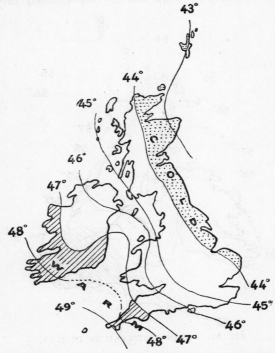

FIG. 12   AVERAGE DAY TEMPERATURE IN JANUARY.

the colder land surface, just as the northward loop over the Irish
Sea is caused by the warmer air over the water. The main land
surface of England in January is lower than that of Eire, and consequently the isotherm 42°F. is forced south as far as Devon. The
warmer English Channel then turns the isotherm east.

This last paragraph is most important because it contains the
explanation of the factors governing temperature distribution
over the British Isles in winter.

In summer these factors are reversed. Now the temperature over the land is higher than over the sea, because the sea warms more slowly than the land. In Figure 11, showing mean temperature for July, it will be noticed that the isotherms now loop in a reverse direction over Eire and the Irish Sea. Follow the line of isotherm 60°F. and notice these effects. Durham is as warm as the west coast of Wales. Observe, too, that places on the east coast of England have a higher mean temperature than those on the west in the same latitude. It is contrary to the popular idea

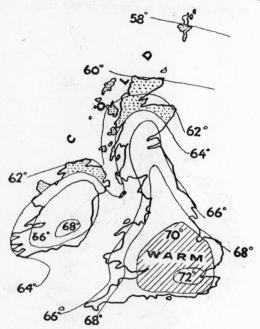

FIG. 13. AVERAGE DAY TEMPERATURE IN JULY.

of things to find Yarmouth warmer than Aberystwyth, and Margate warmer than Ilfracombe.

Let us turn to mean maximum and mean minimum temperatures, which we may regard as day and night values. Two places may have the same mean temperature but may differ by day and night. For instance, York and the Scilly Isles have each a mean temperature of 61°F. in July, but by day York averages 69°F. compared with 65°F. at Scilly, and at night Scilly is warmer than

York. In July there is an average difference of 16°F. between day and night at York, compared with 9½°F. at Scilly.

Average temperature is now recognised not to be an entirely fixed value. Temperature averages are now revised once every five years. Variations are small between one thirty year period and another, but we do know that the winters from 1901 to 1930 were about one degree warmer than from 1871 to 1900.

Someone once remarked: "It is a well-known fact that Bournemouth is the hottest place in England." Like some other "well-known facts" in meteorology, it simply is not true. A gentleman,

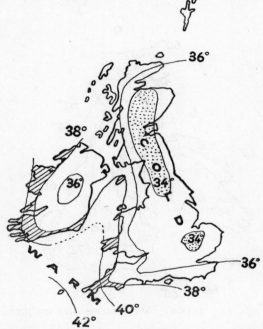

FIG. 14.   AVERAGE NIGHT TEMPERATURE IN JANUARY.

having returned from a summer holiday at Torquay, said: "The heat at Torquay was tremendous, you know. Of course, it is subtropical." As a matter of fact, the mean day temperature at Torquay in July is 68.4°, or one degree less than that of the Midland city he lived in. Now, it is perfectly true that Torquay has not a bracing climate; it is relaxing. What makes a climate relaxing? That is not a simple question, and we must leave it for a later chapter.

The lowest mean annual temperature shown in official records of the British Isles is 43°F. at Braemar, situated at a height of 1,100 feet, in the Upper Dee Valley, Aberdeenshire. It is known that the mean temperature on the summit of Ben Nevis, 4,406 feet, is 31½°F., but no one is likely to build a "highly desirable modern residence with all the usual offices" on the top of Britain's highest mountain.

Penzance, the Scilly Isles and the Channel Islands are warmest, with a mean annual temperature of 52°F.

By how much can mean annual temperature in any particular year vary from the average? Ten degrees either way, was a

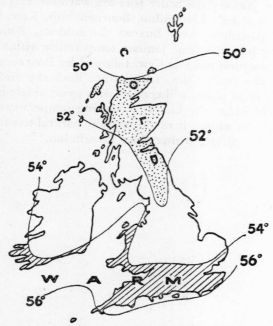

FIG. 15. AVERAGE NIGHT TEMPERATURE IN JULY.

casually expressed opinion. A variation as great as this never occurs. In London and the Midlands, where variations are greatest, the warmest year on record is 3°F. above normal, and the coldest 3°F. below, giving only 6°F. between the hottest and coldest years. At Falmouth the warmest year on record is only 4½°F. above the coldest, while in the Shetlands the warmest and coldest are separated by as little as 3°F. The warmest year on record at Aberdeen is appreciably cooler than an average year at Kew, and the coldest year at Kew is about equal to an ordinary year at Aberdeen. In spite of all the fluctuations of temperature in the course of a year most years as a whole have a mean temperature within a degree or so of the average.

The warmest areas in January are south-west Eire, the Scilly Isles and the toe of Cornwall, and the coldest is a stretch of country from the Fens to East Scotland. In July the greatest warmth centres round London and the Thames Valley, and the coldest parts are northern Scotland, the Orkneys and Shetlands.

And what of those eight places mentioned earlier in the chapter? In January the Scilly Isles are warmest, and the others follow in this order: Llandudno, Bournemouth, Kew, Rothesay, Cambridge, Aberdeen, with Buxton the coldest. Bournemouth and Rothesay have the same January temperature within a degree. In July the warmest place is Kew, followed by Bournemouth and Cambridge, the Scilly Isles, Llandudno, Rothesay and Buxton. The order of these places will conflict with some widely-held ideas. Till one understands the factors governing temperature distribution, especially in winter, it would be quite natural to suppose that Brighton had a milder winter than Llandudno.

CHAPTER VII.

Vagaries of Monthly Temperature

Although the hours of daylight, and therefore of possible sun-shine, are least in December and most in June, the minimum and maximum average levels of temperature are retarded to January and July. February is little warmer than January, the first appreciable rise being in March. After the July maximum a pause occurs and August is almost as warm as July. There is a sharp drop in the thermometer between September and October, and between October and November. December is only slightly milder than January and February. The old saying, "As the days lengthen doth the cold strengthen," is very often true, because the coldest spell of the winter frequently occurs after Christmas.

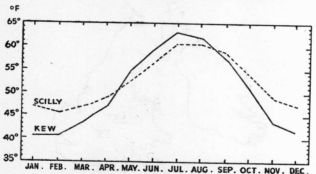

FIG. 16. COMPARISON OF MONTHLY MEAN TEMPERATURE AT KEW AND SCILLY ISLES.

Figure 16 shows the monthly march of temperature at Kew and Scilly. Scilly is warmer than Kew from September to April, and cooler from May to August. July at Kew is 22½°F. warmer than January, but at Scilly the difference between February and July is only 15°F. The coldest month at Scilly is later than at Kew, a feature sometimes met with in very insular climates.

The absence of very hot days at Scilly in summer evokes the question: But what about the sub-tropical gardens at Tresco? Surely these exotic plants need great heat. And what about the palms at Penzance? One might also ask: What about the palms

and fuchsias on the west coast of Scotland? where the summers
are cooler than anywhere in England, except for such bleak
upland regions like the Pennines. This paradox is explained by
the fact that these sub-tropical plants flourish because there is very
little frost in winter in these districts. Palms and fuchsias would
grow very well in most parts of England in summer, but they
could not survive the frosts of winter and spring. No amount of
summer warmth can compensate these plants for winter cold.

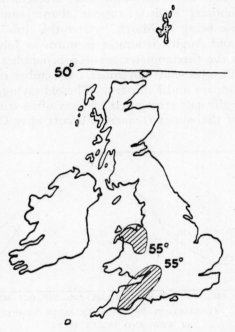

FIG. 17. AVERAGE WARMEST DAY IN JANUARY.

It has been explained how monthly rainfall can vary from the
average in a much greater degree than annual rainfall. In the
same way, monthly temperature can show greater divergences. A
year, as we have seen, 3°F. warmer or colder than usual is very
rare, but in exceptional circumstances a month may be 8°F.
warmer than usual, or 10°F. colder than the average in inland
England, as for example, in December, 1890, February, 1895, and
more recently in January, 1940. Variations in the summer

months are less than in winter, and it is rare for a summer month to be 5°F. warmer than usual.

The warmest January on record in the English Midlands is about equal to the average for Scilly. April in the Midlands has the same mean temperature as Scilly in January. No wonder that the Scilly Isles export early flowers in such quantities. The Scilly Isles in January have a similar mean temperature to the French

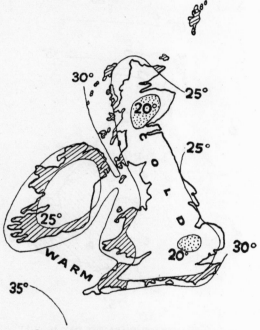

FIG. 18. AVERAGE COLDEST NIGHT IN JANUARY

Riviera, but the two climates are very different. A warm winter day on the Riviera is much warmer than anything ever experienced at Scilly at that season, and on the other hand, the Riviera can at times be subject to frost and snow of an intensity never met with at Scilly or Penzance.

So far, three basic temperatures have been dealt with, mean temperature, mean monthly maximum and mean monthly minimum temperatures. There are four other important points on the thermometric scale, the highest and lowest temperatures on record at any particular place and the average temperature of the

warmest days and coldest nights in each month.   Supposing we
take the month of January at any place for 20 successive years,
picking out the highest and lowest each month, adding together
all the highest and all the lowest and dividing each total by
twenty.   We then obtain temperatures which we may expect there
on the warmest day and coldest night of an average January.

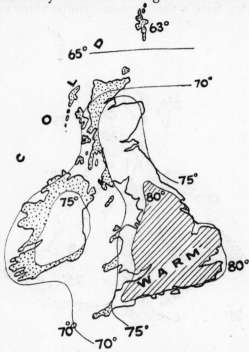

FIG. 19.   AVERAGE WARMEST DAY IN JULY

This process can be carried out for each month, and finally for
the year as a whole.

As an example, if Kew temperatures for June are treated in
this manner over a long period we find the following result:—

JUNE   AT   KEW

					°F.
Highest Temperature on Record	...	...	...	...	91 in 1947
Average Warmest Day	...	...	...	...	80
Average Maximum Temperature	...	...	...	...	68
Mean Temperature	...	...	...	...	59½
Average Minimum Temperature	...	...	...	...	51
Average Coldest Night	...	...	...	...	42
Lowest Temperature on Record	...	...	...	...	37 in 1880 and 1923

If this analysis is carried out for every month in the year at a large number of places throughout the British Isles we obtain a mass of information which enables maps to be drawn showing what may be expected on the warmest days and coldest nights for any month in all parts of the country. Unfortunately, space does not allow a full sequence of these maps to be given, but Figures 17, 18, 19, 20, 21 and 22 show those for January, July and the

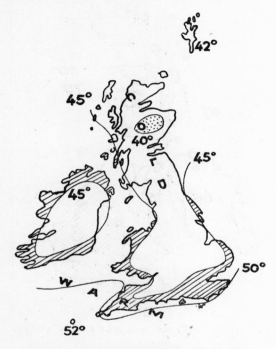

FIG. 20. AVERAGE COLDEST NIGHT IN JULY.

whole year. In January nearly all the British Isles will be from 50°F. to 55°F. on the warmest day. On the coldest night there are small areas below 20°F. and a few points over 30°F. In July most of southern and central England will reach 80°F., and only the extreme north of Scotland fails to reach 70°F. July nights are warmest round the coasts. In Figure 21 it will be noticed that the Midlands, eastern and southern England will touch 85°F. on the year's warmest day and only a few points fail to reach 75°F.

The average warmest day of the year in the Scillies is 71°F., about equal to an average July day in the Midlands. On the coldest night of the year, Figure 22, most of England and Scotland will fall below 20°F. The south-west districts are about 10°F. milder.

Figure 23 is a map showing the highest temperatures on record in the British Isles. At some time or other a temperature of 90°F.

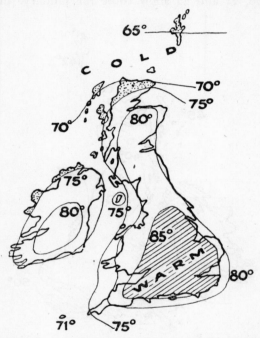

FIG. 21.   AN AVERAGE WARMEST DAY OF A YEAR.

has been reached over almost all England. An area south of the Humber, roughly the south-eastern half of England, has reached 95°F. or over. Hardly any part has failed to reach 80°F., the exceptions being islands off the Scottish coast. The toe of Cornwall has a record maximum several degrees lower than the Edinburgh, Stirling and Perth districts of Scotland. The Scillies, with a record of 82°F., cannot equal the north Scottish mainland with Wick at 85°F. Both the south and east coasts have a high record limit of about 90°F. Margate has touched 94°F. and Scarborough 91°F.

The extremes of cold in this country are mapped in Figure 24. The greater part of England and Scotland have fallen at some time below zero, even as far south as Kent and Sussex. Devon can show lower temperatures than the Shetlands. In the Scilly Isles nothing has been recorded below 25°F.

On an average the warmest day of the year will be about 87°F. in London, 80°F. at Torquay, and 75°F. at Falmouth. The record

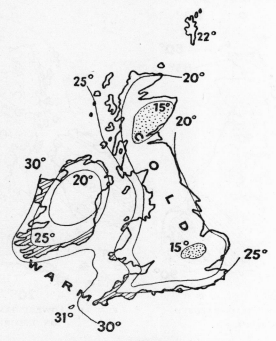

FIG. 22. AN AVERAGE COLDEST NIGHT OF A YEAR.

highs are about 100°F. in London, 87°F. at Torquay, and 85°F. at Falmouth. Some will find these facts difficult to credit, like the old lady when she saw a giraffe for the first time.

The mean temperature of an English winter is focused on a crucial point. A large part of England is near the isotherm of 40°F. (Figure 10). If temperature was 10°F. lower we should have a frozen, snow-covered landscape, but if the thermometer was 10°F. above average, conditions would be virtually those of a normal May. This gives a tremendous contrast for a variation of plus or minus 10°F. Moscow has a January mean temperature of 12°F. This means sharp frost and snow, but if Moscow had a January 10°F. warmer than usual, there would be no perceptible change in the scene, as there would still be frost and snow. At the same time, a January 10°F. colder than usual would still cause

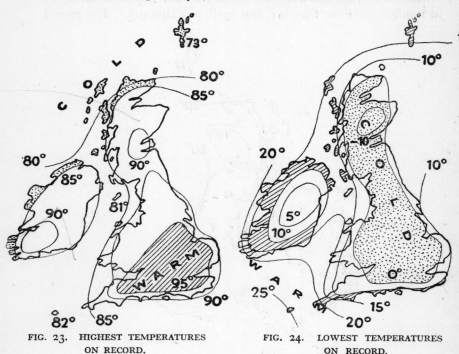

FIG. 23.   HIGHEST TEMPERATURES   FIG. 24.   LOWEST TEMPERATURES
                ON RECORD.   ON RECORD.

no visual change. Sharp frost and snow would simply become more intense frost and snow.

Tables II. and III. supplement this chapter with interesting facts about temperature in January and July for 25 places in the British Isles.

TABLE II.—JANUARY TEMPERATURES

	High Winter Limit	Warm Day January	JANUARY AVERAGES			Cold Night January	Low Winter Limit
			Max.	Mean	Min.		
Shetlands ..	54	49	43.4	40.3	37.1	27	16
Stornoway ..	56	51	44.6	41.2	37.8	25	11
Ben Nevis ..	48	37	27.5	24.1	20.6	11	1
Braemar ..	61	50	40.4	34.9	29.4	13	—17
Aberdeen ..	64	52	43.0	39.0	35.0	22	4
Glasgow ..	56	51	43.4	39.5	35.7	23	6
Douglas, I.O.M.	59	52	45.2	41.5	37.7	29	11
York ..	61	55	44.0	39.5	34.9	25	—5
Liverpool ..	62	53	44.7	40.7	36.7	25	9
Buxton ..	58	49	40.5	36.4	32.3	15	—11
Nottingham ..	62	54	43.9	39.1	34.4	23	—1
Skegness ..	59	53	43.1	38.5	33.8	25	11
Yarmouth ..	60	51	44.3	40.5	36.8	25	10
Kew ..	62	53	44.9	40.5	36.0	22	9
Margate ..	61	54	44.8	40.7	36.7	30	14
Southampton ..	66	54	45.9	40.9	36.0	23	11
Plymouth ..	62	55	47.7	43.1	38.5	27	16
Falmouth ..	58	53	47.7	43.8	39.9	30	19
Scilly Isles ..	58	54	49.3	46.7	44.1	34	25
Jersey ..	62	53	47.4	43.5	39.7	27	12
Llandudno ..	67	57	46.8	42.6	38.4	28	10
Holyhead ..	59	51	46.4	44.0	41.6	29	17
Armagh ..	59	51	45.3	40.6	35.9	22	5
Dublin ..	62	55	47.1	42.7	38.3	27	13
Valentia ..	58	53	48.4	44.9	41.3	29	20

TABLE III.—JULY TEMPERATURES

	High Summer Limit	Warm Day July	July Averages			Cold Night July	Low Summer Limit
			Max.	Mean	Min.		
Shetlands ..	73	63	57.0	55.3	49.5	42	33
Stornoway ..	78	69	60.9	55.7	50.5	41	31
Ben Nevis ..	66	56	44.6	41.1	37.6	30	23
Braemar ..	85	75	63.9	55.1	46.3	37	26
Aberdeen ..	86	73	62.2	56.7	51.2	42	30
Glasgow ..	85	75	64.9	58.7	52.4	44	36
Douglas, I.O.M.	82	71	63.0	57.7	52.3	47	35
York ..	92	82	69.0	60.9	52.9	46	34
Liverpool ..	89	77	65.5	60.0	54.5	49	37
Buxton ..	89	77	64.1	57.1	50.0	40	30
Nottingham ..	94	82	69.1	61.1	53.1	45	34
Skegness ..	89	78	66.4	59.7	52.9	44	36
Yarmouth ..	89	76	67.9	61.7	55.4	47	37
Kew ..	94	82	71.1	63.0	54.9	47	37
Margate ..	94	81	68.5	62.3	56.1	51	39
Southampton ..	92	82	70.4	62.5	54.5	47	37
Plymouth ..	87	77	66.9	61.1	55.2	47	39
Falmouth ..	85	73	66.5	60.8	55.2	50	40
Scilly Isles ..	82	70	65.4	60.6	55.8	52	41
Jersey ..	96	79	68.1	62.3	56.6	49	39
Llandudno ..	93	77	65.9	60.1	54.4	47	37
Holyhead ..	86	72	62.9	59.0	55.1	49	40
Armagh ..	87	75	66.3	58.9	51.5	43	32
Dublin ..	87	75	66.6	60.5	54.4	47	37
Valentia ..	81	71	63.7	59.0	54.3	46	37

CHAPTER VIII.

Sensational Months

Occasionally we experience months of abnormal warmth or cold. March was colder than an average January in 1883, 1917 and 1919, or it may be warmer than an average April, as in 1938. Januarys 1916 and 1921 were nearly as warm as an average April. Accurate statistics do not go back more than a century or less, but there are notes on the weather by ancient writers for a thousand years. It is stated that the Thames was frozen in 1063; that in the winter of 1607-08 the River Ouse was frozen at York and the Thames at Lambeth; that in the winter of 1281-82 five arches of London Bridge were destroyed by the ice. Frost fairs were held on the Thames in the winters of 1715-16 and 1739-40. The accuracy of some of these old records is sometimes questioned. The last frost fair on the Thames was in 1814. Why do not such freeze-ups happen now? This is at least partly due to a change in the river. The channel has been improved to give a quicker flow. In the old days the Thames was more sluggish and therefore more likely to freeze.

Coming to times of which we have reliable information, the coldest months have been Januarys 1838, 1867, 1881 and 1940, and February, 1895. February, 1895, is generally accepted as the coldest month since accurate observations have been made. The mean temperature at Kew was 29.2°F., and at Buxton 24.5°F. Braemar, with a mean of 21.5°F. was the coldest place, and was as much as 14°F. below the average. On February 11th, Braemar reported −17°F., which is still the lowest official screen reading in the British Isles. Other low readings included Buxton −11°F., Stamford, Lincs., −8°F., and Loughborough −5°F. There were ten nights below 0°F. at Braemar in a sequence of fourteen. The Thames was full of floating ice, and the English Lakes had two feet of ice on them. Skating lasted seven weeks in London. Damage to water-pipes underground led to such things being sunk deeper in future. December, 1879, was very cold, and on the 4th, Blackadder, in Berwickshire, became famous by reporting a reading of −23°F., or 55°F. below freezing. In other words, Blackadder was as much below freezing as the hottest day of an

65

ordinary London summer would be above freezing. This reading is not accepted officially as it was not made in a standard screen, but there seems no doubt it was very near the truth. Blackadder again reported −22°F. on January 17, 1881.

In December, 1890, there was skating on the River Witham between Lincoln and Boston, as well as at Nottingham on the River Trent.

In more recent years Februarys 1917 and 1929 were very cold. Some places fell below zero, and in 1929 the ice on Lake Windermere bore the weight of 50,000 skaters. December, 1933, was remarkable for its severe cold in southern England. Barometric pressure was high over northern England, producing a cold easterly wind south of the Humber, and a mild west wind over northern Scotland. The warmest places in Britain were the Hebrides and Shetlands with mean temperatures of 44°F. and 43°F., compared with only 35°F. in London and at Bournemouth, and 33°F. at Tunbridge Wells. The Thames froze above Oxford. At Newquay, where the mean temperature was 37.8°F., it was the coldest December since records began there in 1892. The coldest night of the month at Tavistock, in Devon, was 18°F., forming a strange contrast with the Orkney Islands, where it never fell below 34°F.

January, 1940, was intensely cold, in places the coldest January for at least a century. Nearly all of England and Scotland had a mean temperature below freezing point. In the English Midlands mean temperature was 10°F. below the average. At a number of places temperatures below zero were recorded, the lowest reading of all being −10°F. at Rhayader, in Radnor. Even as far south as Sussex and Kent, −6°F. was registered at Bodiam and −4°F. at Canterbury. Hardly less striking were readings of 3°F. at Killerton and 2°F. at Cullompton, in Devon.

The winter of 1946-1947 was one of the coldest on record. Severe weather prevailed from January 22nd to March 15th over much of the country, and we shivered in what was probably the longest spell of east wind ever known here. It was undoubtedly the snowiest winter of which we have reliable knowledge, and the depth of level snow was as much as 53 inches in Teesdale on February 18th.

In some places the mean temperature in February was the lowest since records began. The lowest official air temperatures in January were −6°F. at Elmstone, Kent, and −5°F. at Writtle,

Essex, and in February −5°F. at Woburn. At Totnes, Devon, the thermometer fell to 4°F. on February 1st.

The effects of great heat are less sensational than those of great cold. Frost covers the landscape with snow and ice, but a hot summer day of 90°F. differs little in appearance from an ordinary one of 70°F. Prolonged great heat and dryness may turn grass brown, however. The four warmest summers in the past 100 years have been 1859, 1868, 1911 and 1933. At Greenwich the warmest July on record was 1859, and the warmest August 1911. Great heat is most striking when accompanied by deficient rainfall, as in 1868, 1911 and 1921. The persistent heat of July, August and the first half of September, 1911, will be remembered by older people. The thermometer reached 80°F. or more on about 40 days in London, the mean day temperature being 81.7°F. in July and 80.8°F. in August, about 8°F. above the average. It was on August 9, 1911, that Greenwich reached its high record of 100°F., but the screen was of an old type. Probably 98°F. would be about the correct figure for that torrid day.

The heat of the summer of 1933 was persistent rather than excessive over short periods. The highest readings in the British Isles were 94°F. at Cambridge and Margate on July 27th.

The hot August of 1911 was followed in 1912 by the coldest August on record. In Nottingham, where the warmest day was only 68°F., it was the sole August which has failed to touch 70°F. since records began in 1867. August, 1902, was also very cold.

March, 1888, was a bitter month and the cold persisted through the summer. In some places that July was the coldest on record, and early on July 11th a light fall of snow occurred over most of the British Isles.

Spring and autumn have their extremes but as they are intermediate seasons the apparent effects are not always so pronounced.

Yet April, 1917, was as sensational a month as one could imagine. It followed a bitter winter, and was as severe an April as any of the past 100 years. At Buxton one night dropped to 8°F., which would be thought very severe in January. Nottingham reported 17°F., Belvoir Castle 10°F., and Worksop, Notts., 7°F. A maximum temperature as low as freezing point is almost unheard-of in April, but Scarborough, on April 2nd, did not exceed 28°F.

At the other extreme, 1893 had an April with day temperature averaging nearly as high as an ordinary June. Just recently,

April, 1943, was unusually warm. March, 1938, broke all records
for warmth in England. At Oxford the mean temperature was
50°F., compared with 47.2°F. in the previous warm March of 1822.
At Tynemouth that March was warmer than a normal May.

In 1927 Edinburgh experienced the coldest June since 1764.
After the warm summer of 1921, October had record warmth in
many places, including London. A high record of 84°F. was
touched in London, 82°F. at Huddersfield, in Yorkshire, and 80°F.
as far north as Kirkcudbright. November, 1938, was the warmest
November for over a century in places. It made meteorological
history when on the 5th 70°F. was recorded officially for the first
time in Britain at several places, such as Cambridge, Clacton,
Chelmsford, Halstead and Tottenham.

Winter mildness is less spectacular than winter cold and probably most people have forgotten December, 1934, which over a
considerable area was the warmest December since records began.
Persistently warm south-west winds blew. In most places the
mean temperature was up to the average for April, or even
higher. At Wick, in the north of Scotland, the temperature
averaged a mere half degree below the average for May. Great
numbers of places did not experience a single night frost. At
Torquay the coldest night was 38°F., at Falmouth 41°F., and in
the Scillies it never fell below 45°F.

What about those old-fashioned winters? Volumes have been
spoken in argument on this topic, and a few ink-pots have been
emptied. It is certainly true that the first thirty years of this
century have had milder winters on the whole than the last thirty
years of the 19th century. From 1876 to 1895 winter temperatures were mainly colder than the average and old people will
recall this period. The question arose, would the mild winters of
the present century continue indefinitely? It has been answered
in the negative by the three recent winters of 1939-40, 1940-41, and
1941-42, which were the coldest three successive winters for 61
years. These three severe winters were followed by a mild one.
There is thus no evidence of any permanent change.

CHAPTER IX.

What the Thermometer Can Do in a Day

HAVING learned something of how temperature varies monthly, both normally and abnormally, the more intimate daily changes can now be investigated. These changes touch us directly, as shown by such common remarks as, "It's turned cooler," "It's warmer than yesterday," "It's chilly after the shower," and so on.

On an "ideal" day, temperature is lowest about sunrise, increases till the afternoon, pauses, and cools again in the evening. By "ideal" day is meant a day on which the temperature rises and falls in a smooth curve. Such days, in practice, are uncommon for so many things may interrupt the harmony of the curve. A passing cloud, a shower, a shift of wind, all affect the thermometer. In the daytime the passing of a cloud will normally cause a drop in temperature, but on a still clear night it would cause a rise. By day the cloud cuts off the warming rays of the sun; by night the cloud checks the loss of heat into space. On a calm, clear night, too, a gentle breeze will raise the temperature. This is because on such nights the air near the ground cools more rapidly than that some feet above it, and the sudden breeze will cause the warmer air to mix with the colder. It follows that cloudless weather favours warm days (except in winter) and cold nights. In other words, the difference in temperature between day and night is greater than the average in cloudless weather, while in cloudy, windy or rainy weather the difference in temperature between day and night will be smaller than usual. Owing to the strength of the sun's rays and the longer period of daylight the difference between day and night is greater in summer than in winter.

At Kew, in July, the average maximum is 71°F., and the average minimum 55°F., a range of 16°F., but in January the range is 9°F., from 36°F. to 45°F. In winter the effect of the sun is so reduced owing to the small angle of the rays and the short period of daylight, that a change in the direction of the wind may quite override its influence. A mild south-west wind might be blowing on a January day with the thermometer at 11 a.m. at 50°F. A shift of wind to north-west with a rise in the barometer might drop the temperature to 43°F. at noon, although the sun was shining. The reverse effect is quite common in winter. It might be calm and frosty at 5 p.m., with a temperature of 30°F., but a falling barometer would indicate an approaching depression. The sky would cloud over, and by 6 p.m. the thermometer might read 34°F. If a south-west wind then set in the temperature might easily rise to 44°F. by midnight. Thus the normal night fall in temperature may be swamped by current weather changes.

On January 7, 1939, about four inches of snow were lying at 9 a.m. at Woodthorpe, Notts., with a temperature of 36°F. after a night of 28°F. At 1 p.m. the thermometer was at 40°F., by 6 p.m. at 47°F., and by 10 p.m. 49°F. The snow had practically disappeared by 9 p.m. and this sudden melting sent a rush of water into a valley to flood the Nottingham to Mansfield road and disorganise traffic at one point. This is an excellent example of a sudden change with a south wind and a falling barometer.

In considering rainfall we adopted a convenient "yard-stick" which we could use to test the significance of heavy rains. In dealing with temperature it is less easy to use this method. The difficulty is that a different "yard-stick" is needed each month and in different districts. Everyone knows that a temperature of 80°F. in the screen (or shade as it is popularly called) is high for a summer day anywhere in Britain, and at the other end of the scale 30°F. is cold and freezing. A temperature of 90°F. in London on a summer day is very uncommon, but 60°F. in January is even more so. Indeed, 60°F. has not been reached at Greenwich in January in the past 100 years.

Table IV. shows vital temperatures for each month at three places, an inland lowland locality (Cambridge), a south-west maritime place (Falmouth), and Aberdeen, on the east coast of Scotland.

Using this Table one can see that at Cambridge an average July afternoon reaches 71°F., and a day of 84°F. would be decidedly warm, while at Falmouth a July day of 71°F. would be warm, and one of 84°F. almost record height. Space does not allow a sequence of these tables to be given for a considerable number of places.

At the majority of places in the British Isles the maximum temperature on the coldest day of the year will be within a degree or two of freezing point either way. Only at such insular places as Falmouth, Scilly, Valentia and Douglas is the coldest day 4°F.

or more above freezing. The temperature of the warmest night is also fairly uniform over the country. Our sensation of warmth or cold varies with the season. In winter a temperature of 48°F. will feel mild and 53°F. very mild, but these temperatures would feel cold in May. In April 65°F. would feel warm, but in summer would seem rather cool, and 60°F. cold.

The highest and lowest temperatures in the British Isles in some recent years are as follows:—

	Maxima	Minima
1935	92° F. at Attenborough, Notts.	4° F. at Braemar.
1936	89° F. in London.	5° F. at Braemar.
1937	92° F. Canterbury and Tunbridge Wells.	−7° F. at Braemar.
1938	87° F. London and Reading.	4° F. at Braemar.
1939	90° F. in London.	1° F. at Dalwhinnie and Braemar.
1940	91° F. at Cranwell, Lincs.	−10° F. at Rhayader (Radnor).
1941	94° F. in London.	−6° F. at Houghall (Durham) and West Linton.
1942	93° F. at Sprowston (Norfolk).	−3° F. at Braemar.
1943	93° F. at Worcester and Croydon.	7° F. at Braemar.
1944	91° F. in London, at Tunbridge Wells and Horsham.	5° F. at Braemar.
1945	90° F. at Norwich and Whitstable.	−3° F. at Dalwhinnie.
1946	87° F. in London, Finningley (Yorkshire) and Maldon (Essex).	6° F. at Dalwhinnie.
1947	94° F. in London and at Waddington (Lincs.).	−6° F. at Elmstone (Kent), Houghall (Durham), Peebles & Braemar.
1948	95° F. at Milford (Surrey).	4° F. at Logie Goldstone (Aberdeenshire).

If we extract figures like this for twenty years, add them up and divide by twenty, we find that on an average the extreme variation of temperature in Britain in the course of a year is from 91°F. to 3°F.

A night as warm as 60°F. is not common, and few places exceed 65°F. on the year's warmest night. A rare event is a night with a minimum of 70°F. On July 12, 1923, Hampstead did not fall below 71°F. Brighton, St. Leonards and Tavistock each reported the same value that month. At Ventnor the night of July 12-13, 1923, never fell below 72°F., and on August 20, 1932, Lympne, in Kent, experienced a night of 73°F. When unusually warm nights occur the weather is generally unsettled and cloudy. A very hot day of 80°F. will as a rule be followed by a night below 60°F. if the air is dry and the sky fairly free from cloud. The hot nights mentioned above occurred in thundery weather, which would make them feel all the more oppressive. During the night of July 13-14, 1926, a minimum of 70°F. was reported as far north as Lancaster.

TABLE IV.—VITAL TEMPERATURE POINTS

CAMBRIDGE

	High Limit	Warm Day	Average Day	Average Night	Cold Night	Low Limit
January ..	59	54	45	34	20	4
February ..	67	56	46	33	21	1
March	70	63	50	34	23	11
April	84	69	55	38	26	21
May	88	75	63	44	30	25
June	93	81	68	48	38	31
July	95	84	71	52	43	36
August ..	96	83	71	52	42	38
September ..	93	78	66	48	36	28
October ..	80	68	58	42	29	23
November ..	70	59	49	37	24	8
December ..	60	55	45	35	21	0

FALMOUTH

	High Limit	Warm Day	Average Day	Average Night	Cold Night	Low Limit
January ..	56	53	48	40	30	19
February ..	58	53	48	40	31	21
March ..	63	55	50	40	32	24
April ..	69	60	53	43	36	29
May	75	66	59	48	40	35
June	82	70	63	52	46	40
July	85	73	67	55	50	44
August ..	80	71	67	55	50	44
September ..	78	68	63	53	45	36
October ..	72	62	58	48	39	32
November ..	62	57	52	43	35	23
December ..	58	54	49	41	32	24

ABERDEEN

	High Limit	Warm Day	Average Day	Average Night	Cold Night	Low Limit
January ..	59	52	43	35	22	4
February ..	64	53	43	35	22	6
March ..	66	59	45	36	24	10
April	74	62	48	38	29	21
May	75	68	53	43	33	29
June	80	72	59	47	38	30
July	86	73	62	51	42	38
August ..	81	73	62	51	40	33
September ..	82	69	58	47	36	30
October ..	77	64	52	43	31	25
November ..	62	56	46	38	26	13
December ..	60	53	44	36	22	6

Over the eastern half of England south of the Humber (except in coastal places) the thermometer will reach or exceed 80°F. in the screen on from six to ten days a year. Over the London area the number is twelve. The Midland city of Nottingham averages six days a year with 80°F., affording a striking contrast to Falmouth, where it takes about half a century to register six such days. The Scilly Isles had a reading of 82°F. on July 11, 1921, and this appears to be the only day to reach 80°F. in these islands in the past 70 years. Douglas, in the Isle of Man, has had five days with 80°F. in 70 years.

How much can temperature vary in the course of a day in Britain? It depends on the season of the year and the locality. At Kew, the average daily variation varies from 9°F. in January to 17°F. in May and June, with 13°F. for the year as a whole. There are not many places with an average daily variation of 15°F. for the year, but Cambridge, Chelmsford, Marlborough, South Farnborough, Reading, Shrewsbury, Worcester and Worksop average 16°F., and Welshpool 17°F. On individual days some very wide divergences from average values may occur. As one may expect the greatest ranges between day and night take place in inland districts, and the least ranges occur on small islands. The greatest divergences of all take place in inland valleys. The ranges vary with the weather, being least in unsettled, windy, rainy weather with a low or falling barometer, and greatest during a spell of calm, cloudless weather with a high barometer. At inland places temperature may vary 30°F. in a day, and in exceptional conditions the value may reach or exceed 40°F. in some places. In a valley near Rickmansworth a range of 51°F. was recorded on August 29, 1936, a night of 34°F. being followed by a day of 85°F.—an extraordinary divergence, and the largest night-day change on British records. In the dry anticyclonic weather of March, 1929, great ranges were reported. At Attenborough, Notts., on March 9, 1929, a night of 23°F. (which would be a sharp frost in January) was followed by an afternoon of 70°F. (a July height), a difference of 47° in a few hours.

What a range of 40°F. in one day means may be better appreciated by using three "yard-sticks." First, the mean maximum at Kew on a July day is 26°F. higher than on a January day; second, a range of 40°F. between the warmest day and coldest night in the course of *one month* is fairly large; third, on an average the coldest night of the year at Scilly is 31°F. and the warmest day

71°F. In other words, the temperature at some inland localities may vary more in about 12 hours than it does in a whole year in the Scilly Isles, a fact so remarkable as to sound almost incredible.

On June 3, 1939, the maximum temperature at Woodthorpe, Notts., was 71°F., with cloudless weather, dry air and an east wind. The following night it fell to 35°F., a drop of 36°F., but this was followed a few hours later the same day by 77°F. Not only was there a great range of 42°F. on June 4th, but two days of over 70°F. were separated by a night close to freezing point.

How does it come about that temperature can rise and fall so many degrees in a few hours? In fine weather, with a high barometer and dry air, the atmosphere near the ground loses its heat very rapidly by radiation into space. At sunrise there is thus a shallow layer of cold air close to the ground with warm air above it (for air at a few thousands of feet cools little at night). Imagine, then, a powerful sun beating on the ground after sunrise. The shallow layer of cold air must warm up very rapidly in these circumstances. It suffers the fate of a snowball in an oven. If instead of warm air above, a mass of cold humid air covered the country, even in sunshine, we should not experience a rapid increase of warmth by day.

Sometimes with a change of weather a large alteration in temperature will take place in a short period. At Nottingham on September 11, 1919, after a night of 51°F., and a morning fog followed by brilliant sunshine the thermometer rose to 85°F., a very high level for mid-September. A gentle breeze blew from the south. The following day, September 12th, was overcast with a north-east wind and the temperature never rose about 56°F., *above* which felt very cold by contrast.

A rapid change of temperature may occasionally develop in a very short space of time. On Easter Monday, April 21, 1924, there was a very rapid change from warmth to cold. At Worksop, Notts., the morning was fine and very warm for the season, reaching 72.6°F. just before 2 p.m. The sky then clouded over quickly and the thermometer had dropped to 53°F. by 3 p.m. Here is a case of temperature falling 20°F. in a single hour at a time of day when the thermometer should be at its greatest height and pausing lazily prior to its normal decline towards evening. Such a sudden lapse was not due merely to the sky clouding over and at that time of day certainly not caused by radiation into space. The cause was a sudden inrush of cold air from the north-west displacing the warm air.

In contrast to these wide divergences there are periods when daily ranges are small. It is not easy to say how little the thermometer may vary in 24 hours, but perhaps it is 5°F., or rather less on some days. On January 26, 1942, the author recorded a range as small as 1.2°F. Unfortunately, owing to conditions under which records of maximum and minimum temperatures are kept this value does not represent the truth. Let us examine what happens. On January 26, 1942, at the morning visit to the screen, the night minimum had been 28.0°F., which was entered as the minimum for the 26th, in accordance with the rules. The maximum thermometer registered 43.7°F., and this was entered as the maximum for the 25th. The thermometers were then set. Next morning, January 27th, the minimum thermometer showed 21.0°F. (entered as the minimum for the 27th) and the maximum thermometer showed 29.2°F. as the maximum for the 26th. The entries for the 26th were thus, maximum 29.2°F. and minimum 28.0°F., and range 1.2°F. Actually, the variation of temperature on the 26th was more than this. There is little doubt that the maximum of 29.2°F. occurred soon after setting the thermometer on the morning of the 26th. At 1 p.m. the temperature was 27.6°F.; at 6 p.m. 24.6°F., and at 10 p.m. 22.2°F. It is therefore obvious that the range on the 26th was at least 7°F., and the apparent small range was due to accidental causes. This difficulty would disappear if thermometers were read and set at midnight daily. A thermograph would solve the problem, but many observers choose to spend their money on food and the education of their children. Fortunately, it is not often that temperature ranges are vitiated in this way.

An authentic case of remarkable temperature stability was given in the Scilly Isles in December, 1934. Not only was the mean daily range as small as 4°F., but the warmest day of 54°F. was separated from the coldest night of the month, 45°F., by a mere 9°F.

How a heat wave affects the British Isles is shown in Figures 25, 26, and 27. On June 21, 1935, the barometer was high to the east and low to the west of our islands, giving a southerly air current. Two days later inland England and part of southern Scotland reached 80°F. or over. Similar conditions prevailed on June 24th and 25th. On June 26th the heat wave was collapsing with cooler air spreading in from the west.

Here are a few extremes of high and low temperatures which have been recorded :—

						Maxima	Minima
Dundee	...	...	...	...	...	87° F.	4° F.
Leith ...	...	...	...	...	...	90°	6°
Rothesay	...	...	...	...	...	85°	11°
Durham	...	...	...	...	...	89°	—1°
Scarborough	...	...	...	...	...	91°	8°
Sheffield	...	...	...	...	...	92°	6°
Cheltenham	...	...	...	...	...	93°	—3°
Oxford	...	...	...	...	...	95°	3°
Canterbury	...	...	...	...	...	98°	—4°
Margate	...	...	...	...	...	94°	14°
Worthing	...	...	...	...	...	90°	13°
Ventnor	...	...	...	...	...	90°	15°
Bournemouth	...	...	...	...	...	93°	14°
Cullompton	...	...	...	...	...	92°	2°
Bude ...	...	...	...	...	...	89°	4°

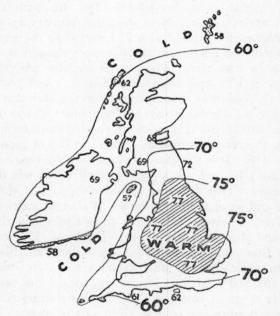

FIG. 25.   JUNE 21, 1935.   BEGINNING OF A HEAT-WAVE.
SOUTHERLY WIND CURRENT OVER BRITAIN.

Travellers' Tales

Most of us have listened to travellers' tales, and very entertaining they are sometimes. Here are three brief ones. "It was 120°F. in the shade, old boy." "You ought to go to Spain to feel real heat. It was 120°F. in the shade when I was there." "When

I was in Portugal the heat was terrific, 130°F. in the shade."
None of the three gentlemen who told these tales was an inten-
tional liar. They simply had not the facts. A temperature of
120°F. in the shade is uncommon anywhere. At Khartoum, in
the Sudan, the average maximum day temperature for the whole
year is 98°F., a very great heat, but the highest on record is
no more than 117°F. Aswan, Egypt, has slightly exceeded 120°F.

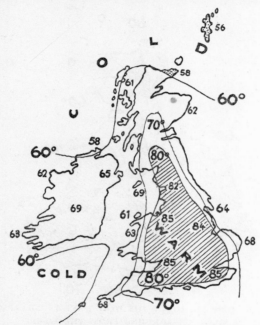

FIG. 26. JUNE 23, 1935. THE HEAT-WAVE COVERS
ENGLAND.

As regards our Spanish traveller, if he happened to experience
a very hot spell while there, it might possibly have reached 100°F.
in the shade or a little more. In Madrid, the average day temperature in July is 90°F., and on an average the hottest day of the
year reaches 104°F. The highest on record at Madrid is 112°F.
The hottest part of Spain is the valley of the River Guadalquivir,
where the average afternoon peak temperature in summer is
nearly 100°F., but even here the extreme limit is about 115°F.
The highest temperature on record in Rome is 108°F., and at
Algiers 112°F. Portugal has never experienced anything like as

high as 130°F. The highest authentic screen temperatures in the
world are 134°F. in Death Valley, California, on July 10, 1913,
and 136° F. at Azizia, Tripoli, on September 13, 1922.

Let us listen again for a moment to our travellers talking. "It
was 120°F. in the shade, old boy." "Bournemouth's the hottest

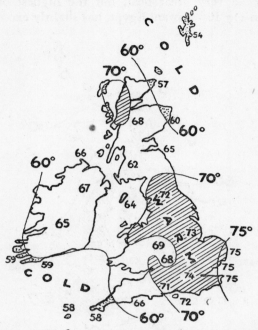

FIG. 27. JUNE 26, 1935. THE HEAT-WAVE IS COLLAPSING.
COOLER AIR ARRIVING FROM THE WEST.

place in England." "The heat at Torquay is quite tropical, you
know."

Enjoy travellers' tales if you wish, but please do not believe
them without reliable scientific confirmation.

CHAPTER X.

BINDING FROST AND MELTING SUN

FROST is simply a fall in temperature below the freezing-point of water, 32°F. In our islands prolonged frost is uncommon, and in a mild winter serious frost may be almost absent, even in inland districts. We do not experience the weeks of frost that are natural to Central and Eastern Europe, and with us ice of sufficient thickness for skating does not often form. One of the most prolonged frosts of modern times was that of January and February, 1895, rather more than two months.

What is a frosty night? Rather an absurd question? Any-one who keeps a record of temperature knows that sometimes the grass is covered with hoar frost with the thermometer in the screen several degrees above freezing. There are, in fact, two types of frost, a true air frost as shown by the screened thermometer and the ground frost. A thermometer exposed on the ground usually falls several degrees lower at night than in the screen, for radiation is more rapid on or near the ground than a few feet above it. The Press, in reporting night temperatures in cold weather, seems to prefer the grass minimum, perhaps because the frost is more intense and sounds more sensational. The meteorologist is usually more concerned with frost in the screen, as this means a true air frost at the level of a person's body and face. Ground frost can be very important in spring, for it can do great damage to early vegetables and fruit blossom.

Can you recognise hoar-frost? On a cool September morning a man once said, "Yes, autumn is coming on. You can see the frosses on the grasses of a morning." Another person said on an autumn day which had opened with a white frost and turned mild under a strong sun, "It's odd how the white frost stays on the grass now it is warm." Neither of these gentlemen had taken the trouble to look at their "white-frost." Had they bent down they would have seen that it was not frost at all, but dew shining in the sun. It is important in meteorology not to be misled by appearances.

As was stated in the last chapter, even the coldest day of the year is not much below freezing point in most places. Even in

severe spells of frost it is common for the thermometer to rise a
few degrees above 32° F. during the afternoons. Not many
statistics on this point are available, but it freezes all day on an
average on eight days a year at Eskdalemuir, four days at
Nottingham, three days at Cambridge and Kew, two days at
Aberdeen and Southport, one day in two years at Douglas, Isle of
Man, and one day in four years at Falmouth. In the severe
February of 1895, when most of Britain was in the iron grip of a
great frost, the afternoon temperatures averaged 35° F. at Oxford
and 36° F. at York and London, and these values were typical. In
the recent severe January of 1940 the same thing was in
evidence, the mean day maximum being 34° F. at York, 35° F. at
Nottingham, Birmingham and Canterbury, and 36° F. in London.
Ice will remain unthawed and snow lie crisp and dry with an air
temperature several degrees above freezing, provided the sky is
clear. This is because a clear sky allows radiation from the
ground and so keeps the temperature there below freezing.

The following short list, taken from data compiled by Miss L.
F. Lewis, shows the average number of nights with frost in the
screen in a year at various places. It emphasises what has been
learnt about the effect of insularity.

		Screen Frost per annum
Ben Nevis, 4,406 feet	... ...	248
Eskdalemuir, Dumfries	... ...	110
Morpeth	... ...	70
Cambridge	... ...	70
Renfrew	... ...	64
Nottingham ...	... ...	64
Dublin ...	... ...	62
Norwich	... ...	54
Oxford	... ...	52
Kew ...	... ...	46
Southampton	... ...	46
Aberdeen	... ...	44
Birmingham ...	... ...	41
Southport	... ...	39
Rothesay ...	... ...	27
Orkney Islands	... ...	24
Douglas, Isle of Man	... ...	17
Falmouth	... ...	13
Valentia	... ...	12
Holyhead	... ...	6

Notice that Kew, Southampton and Aberdeen have a similar
frost frequency, and that a night's frost in the Orkneys is about
half as likely to occur as in London. These facts conflict with
"popular" ideas on the subject. Night frost is most frequent in-

land, but is subject to marked local variations, as we shall see in a later chapter.

There are two types of air frost. One is radiation frost, which occurs on calm, clear nights and may be followed by a mild, sunny day in spring and autumn. Radiation frost may be local in valleys. This usually happens with west, through north to east winds and does not often occur with south or south-west winds. It frequently develops in spring in the rear of a passing depression. The west, at sunset, is flushed a placid red, the air falls still with smoke rising lazily, a haze appears on the horizon. When these signs appear the gardener should take precautions, especially in April and May.

The other type of air frost is wind frost. A wind frost only occurs in winter when an easterly current is blowing from a frost-bound continent. This type of weather is most bitter and searching. The wind is dry and cutting, the sky often overcast, and temperature in the daytime very little above that at night.

An excellent example of frost brought on the wings of an east wind from the continent happened in December, 1938. A moderate east wind set in on December 17th over South-East England. Frost set in by evening. On December 18th and 19th the wind was about gale force with a maximum temperature below freezing over much of England. On the 20th the maximum temperature was no higher than 27° F. at Kew and Bournemouth, 28° F. at Nottingham, and 30° F. at Skegness, Guernsey and Falmouth. This was the lowest December maximum recorded at Falmouth since 1890. It was Kent, nearest to the continent, which was most severely affected, and at Lympne the thermometer never rose above 22° F. This frost was most intense and prolonged in Kent. At Manston it froze continuously for 147 hours, and at Lympne for 222 hours, except for a break of five hours in the forenoon of December 24th. In the severe frost of February, 1929, the temperature at Manston remained below freezing-point from 11 p.m. on February 10th to 9 a.m. on the 20th, a period of no less than 226 hours of unbroken frost. This was quite eclipsed during February, 1947, when Oxford recorded 372 hours of continuous frost, and Woodthorpe, Notts., 320 hours.

When a frost of this character occurs it is not uncommon for Kent to suffer badly, as the wind from the continent does not warm much in passing over the narrow sea. Up the East Coast

F

the sea widens and so is able to exert a greater warming influence
on a freezing east wind.

Although the maximum temperature does not often fail to
reach 30° F., considerably lower values occasionally occur. An
extraordinarily severe frost affected Scotland in November, 1919.
On November 14th the minimum thermometer at Braemar fell
to −10° F., but what is even more remarkable it never rose above
12° F. during the day, and Balmoral eclipsed this with a maximum of 10° F. This is probably the lowest maximum recorded
in Britain this century, but on December 24, 1860, the thermometer
at Paisley is stated not to have risen above the Arctic level of 3½° F.

On December 17, 1927, Logie Coldstone, in Aberdeenshire,
never rose about 13° F., and Balmoral 15° F. Renfrew's maximum on December 23, 1935, was 18° F. In England, Buxton did
not exceed 20° F. on February 13, 1929, and Roden, Shropshire,
had the same maximum next day. Another very cold day was
December 29, 1939, when the thermometer at Barton Airport,
near Manchester, varied from a minimum of 8° F. to a maximum
of 19°F. More recently, on January 24, 1945, the maximum
temperature was as low at 18° F. at York and 15° F. at Leeming
(North Riding); and on January 26, 1945, 18° F. at Hawarden and
16° F. at Wrexham.

Summer Frosts

Frost can occur in the summer months of June, July and
August. It is certainly not common, and many places have never
recorded such an event, including Kew and Greenwich. In June
frost has developed as far south as Wiltshire and Hampshire,
such as 30° F. at Marlborough in June, 1890 and 1893. St.
Albans reported 31° F. in June, 1923. A reading as low as 26° F.
occurred at Balmoral and Braemar in June, 1936. Few places
have registered frost in July. A search through official records
shows frost sometime in July at Wick, Balmoral, Braemar, West
Linton (Peebles), Wolfelee (Roxburgh), Buxton, Armagh and
Stornoway, and there may be a few other places. On July 10,
1918, West Linton fell to 28° F. In the warm, dry July of 1921
Buxton had one night down to 31° F., a striking case of strong
nocturnal radiation in fine weather. In August, 1932, Balmoral
reported 28° F., and on August 30, 1885, Alston, in the North
Pennines, fell to 27° F.

When water cools it increases in density till a temperature of

39° F. is reached, when it begins to expand on further cooling.
Ice then floats on water. This is a most important dispensation.
If ice sank we should have lakes and rivers freezing solid from the
bottom upwards, so that summer thawing would be slow and
difficult, rendering large areas now populated unfit for habitation.

Temperature in the Sun

The ordinary thermometer is not much use for taking temperatures in the sun. If such a thermometer is exposed it will
read lower than the true sun temperature because it will be
surrounded by much cooler air. So special thermometers have
been devised with the bulb enclosed in a glass shield from which
air has been exhausted to form a vacuum. As a bright mercury
bulb reflects some of the heat it is painted black so that no heat
is lost from this source.

It is well to remember that the temperature shown by this
special thermometer is not strictly a natural one. The black bulb
thermometer may be regarded as showing the temperature
developed when the electro-magnetic energy of the sun's rays are
transformed into heat as they impinge upon it. Not very many
places keep a record of sun temperature.

In the summer months a reading of 115° F. or 120° F. is quite
ordinary for the black bulb, and it is sometimes 60° F. or more
higher than the temperature of the air. At times readings of
140° F. or 150° F. happen in this country. On an average of 16
years the highest reading during the summer at Greenwich is
150° F. A five years' average at Nottingham shows that the
mean daily maximum temperature in the sun is about 60° F. in
December and January, 95° F. in April, 115° F. in June, July and
August, and 90° F. in October.

In July, 1925, the sun thermometer reached the very great
height of 173°F. at Greenwich; on July 7, 1930, 175°F. at
Rickmansworth. Even in the hottest parts of the world this
figure is not often exceeded. In January, 1914, Coolgardie, in
Western Australia, registered 184° F. Temperatures in the sun
can be very extreme in high mountain regions. While in the
Karakoram Mountains in Asia, Dr. and Mrs. Workman recorded
a sun temperature of 204° F., almost the boiling point of water,
on July 28, 1903, the shade temperature at the time being given
as 56° F. So far as can be ascertained, nothing to equal this has
been observed near sea-level in the tropics.

CHAPTER XI.

SENSATIONAL DAYS

ALTHOUGH our climate is noteworthy for the absence of great temperature extremes such as are endured by dwellers on the continental land masses, it can in exceptional circumstances give samples of a sensational nature. This chapter is a diary giving some of these events during the present century.

Aug. 31-Sept. 3, 1906.—A heat wave of unprecedented intensity for so late in the season. Over much of England the temperature rose to 90° F. or more on three or four successive days. Nottingham: Maxima, Aug. 31, 93° F.; Sept. 1, 92.8° F.; Sept. 2, 94.2° F.; Sept. 3, 89.8° F. Bawtry, Notts., touched 96° F. on Sept. 2nd, a high record for Britain in September. The thermometer reached 89° F. as far north as Paisley.

April 24, 1908.—An intensely cold polar current swept the country. Night minima fell as low as 11° F. at Carlisle and 10° F. at Balmoral. At Huddersfield a night of 19° F. in the screen and 9° F. on the grass was followed by a low day maximum of 34° F.

Dec. 29-30, 1908.—Two very keen days. In London the maximum temperature of 29th was 23° F. and the minimum 21° F. On the 30th the thermometer varied between 13° F. and 24° F.

March, 1909.—The opening days were snowy and very cold. In London temperature fell to 14° F. and at Marlborough to 0° F.

Aug. 9, 1911.—In many places this was the warmest day on record. In the London area temperature was 95° F. to 99° F. At Lincoln 96° F. was reached, and by evening the leaves on large trees were hanging limp like those of a plant which has just been transplanted.

April 17, 1912.—An eclipse of the sun took place with over ninety per cent. of the sun's disc obscured in the London district. Figure 28 shows the temperature curve at Walthamstow. The weather was cloudless with an east wind. During the eclipse the temperature fell 6° F., the lowest point being a quarter of an hour after the maximum phase.

May 12-13, 1915.—Two very cold days with rain and a north to north-east wind. At Lincoln the maxima were 42° and 43° F., a January level.

Feb. 7, 1917.—A very cold day. At Nottingham the temperature varied from 10° F. to 26° F.

April 1-2, 1917.—A very severe spell. The maximum temperature at Nottingham on 1st was 31° F., and 28° F. at Scarborough on 2nd. The minima were extremely low in the north and Midlands on the 2nd. Among the lowest tem-

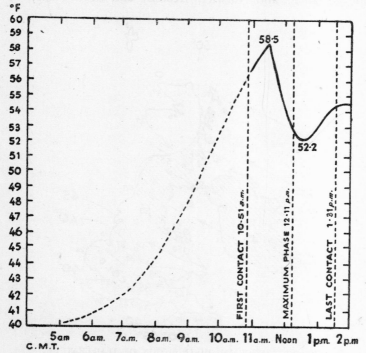

FIG. 28. TEMPERATURE AT WALTHAMSTOW, LONDON, DURING THE SOLAR ECLIPSE OF APRIL 17, 1912.

peratures were 5° F. at Newton Rigg, 6° F. at Eskdalemuir, 7° F. at Rounton (Yorks.) and Worksop, 8° F. at Balmoral, Braemar and Buxton, 10° F. at Burnley, Wakefield and Belvoir Castle, and 11° F. at York. All these temperatures are phenomenal for April.

July 10-11, 1921.—This was the peak of a very warm July. On the 10th temperature reached 92° F. at Lincoln and Notting-

ham, and on 11th 93° F. in London and at Canterbury, and
94° F. at Woking.

October 6, 1921.—In what was the warmest October on record in
many places this was the warmest day. Temperature rose to
84° F. in London, and 83° F. at a number of places. Bath,
Weston-super-Mare and Huddersfield touched 82° F.

May 22-23, 1922.—A remarkable heat wave with record May temperatures. In London 91° F. was attained. Bexley Heath
logged 90° F., and Norwich, Reading and Grain (Kent) 89° F.

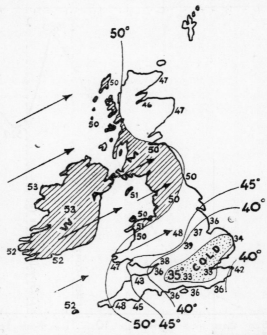

FIG. 29. ABNORMAL DISTRIBUTION OF TEMPERATURE,
DEC. 11, 1924. CALM AND FOGGY OVER SOUTH-EAST
ENGLAND. MILD SOUTH-WEST WIND OVER REST OF
COUNTRY.

July 11-13, 1923.—This was a very hot spell in which numerous
places south of the Humber reached 90° F. or more. In
London 96° F. was touched. Hitchin and Clifton reported
95° F. Further north, Norwich had 93° F., Nottingham
92° F., Manchester and Lancaster 90° F. Record heat
occurred in Devon and Cornwall, Killerton 94° F., Cullomp-

ton 92° F., Torquay 87° F., and Falmouth, 85° F., all high records since observations began.

December 11, 1924.—An abnormal distribution of temperature gave this day a special interest. Over that part of England east of a line drawn from Dorset to the Wash the wind was light from the east or calm, with considerable fog and low temperature. West and north of this line a mild south-west wind prevailed. In London and at Yarmouth the highest temperature during the day was 34° F. Littlehampton, Bournemouth and Bath registered 36° F. In the mild area, Nottingham rose to 48 F., Blackpool 49° F., Penzance and Scarborough 50° F., and Llandudno 51° F. Figure 29 gives a graphic picture of this.

September 19, 1926.—An exceptionally warm day for so late in the season. London 90° F., Hunstanton (Norfolk) 89° F., Cromer and Canterbury 88° F., Chelmsford and Cambridge 87° F., Southend, Halstead, Norwich and Nottingham 86° F. This occurred with a slowly falling barometer and a south-east wind. Next day, with a rising barometer and north-west wind maximum temperatures were about 20° F. lower.

November 2, 1927.—An unusually warm day. A number of places reported 65° F., with a maximum of 67° F. at Tyne-mouth, Geldeston (Norfolk) and Wakefield.

January 30, 1929.—Aber (Bangor) reported 63° F. The same temperature was registered at Rhyl in January, 1916, and Colwyn Bay in January, 1920. This appears to be about the upward limit for the British Isles in January.

March 29, 1929.—On this day temperature soared to 77° F. at Wakefield, probably a record for Britain in March. Killerton (Devon) and Newport, Isle of Wight, touched 74° F., and York 73° F.

August 27-29, 1930.—The most remarkable spell of great heat so late in the season since 1906. A humid southerly wind blew. In London 94° F. was registered, with 90° F. to 92° F. at a number of places. Attenborough, Notts., reached 92° F. on three successive days; 91° F. occurred as far north as Huddersfield. The heat ended in a severe thunderstorm (page 38).

December 24, 1931.—Aberdeen reached the record December high level of 60° F.

August 19, 1932.—A day of extreme heat in the Midlands and South of England. The thermometer rose to 97° F. in London and at Halstead, and 95° F. at Oxford and Reading. Norwich achieved its highest record of 96° F.

March 28, 1933.—In a valley near Rickmansworth a temperature of 19° F. at 5.30 a.m. was followed by 67° F. at 1.30 p.m., a rise of 48° F. in eight hours. On the previous day at 6 p.m. the thermometer showed 60° F., but with intense nocturnal radiation it fell 21° F. in one hour, to 39° F. At Thetford, Norfolk, on March 28th, a minimum of 17° F. was followed by a maximum of 66° F.

June 4-8, 1933.—A spell of brilliantly sunny weather and dry air sent the temperature above 80° F. on five successive days, which is most unusual so early in the summer. In London 89° F. was attained, and 86° F. as far north as Morayshire.

July 4-12, 1934.—A very prolonged spell of great heat. There were nine successive days with 80° F. or more at Nottingham. The highest reported in Britain was 92° F. at Attenborough, Notts. A number of places from Devon to Lancashire reached 90° F. In Scotland 88° F. was touched at Perth and Kilmarnock.

May 17, 1935.—An unusually long and severe cold spell lasted from May 12-19. The frost was most severe on the 17th. In a valley near Rickmansworth the thermometer dropped to 17° F. in the screen and 10° F. on the ground. At Purley it was 24° F., while Marlborough and Tunbridge Wells were down to 25° F. The minimum of 28° F. at Greenwich was equal to the previous low record there for May. Great damage was done to vegetation in Hertfordshire, Buckingham, Worcestershire and Hereford.

June, 1936.—Some sharp frost occurred this month. On June 1st the minimum was 31° F. at Attenborough and Woodthorpe, and 30° F. at Sutton Bonington, all in Nottinghamshire. On the 5th the thermometer slumped to 25° F. at Dalwhinnie (Inverness), and 26° F. at Balmoral and Braemar.

November 5, 1938.—In many places this was the warmest November day on record (page 68).

January 21, 1940.—The night of January 20-21 was the coldest of an exceptionally severe month. A number of places fell below zero. The lowest temperatures reported were −10° F. at Rhayader (Radnor), −7° F. at Llandrindod Wells, −6° F. at Ambleside and Bodiam (Sussex), −5° F. at Dalwhinnie, −4° F. at Canterbury, Welshpool, Hereford, Newport (Shropshire) and Houghall (Durham), −3° F. at Braemar, Droitwich, Worcester and Whitstable, −2° F. at Castleton (Yorks.), Wye (Kent) and Bala (Merioneth) and −1° F. at Buxton and Mayfield (Stafford).

June 6, 1940.—Temperature reached 89° F. at Perth, the highest reading in Scotland since July 12, 1911, when 90° F. was touched.

June 22, 1941.—The hottest June day on record in places. The thermometer rose to 94° F. in London, 92° F. at Huddersfield and Peterborough, and 90° F. at Nottingham and several other places.

August 5, 1942.—Night minimum temperature fell to 31° F. at Newport (Shropshire), the lowest reading in Britain during the month.

July 31, 1943.—A very warm day; 93° F. at Worcester and Croydon.

September 27, 1943.—The thermometer fell to 23° F. at Peebles and Eskdalemuir.

February 29, 1944.—Temperature fell to 9° F. at Mayfield, Walsall, Newport (Shropshire), Belper and Woodthorpe (Notts.).

May 29, 1944.—An exceptionally hot day for May. Temperature reached 91° F. in London, at Horsham and Tunbridge Wells.

August 27, 1944.—Temperature fell as low as 27° F. at Dalwhinnie.

January 26, 1945.—The thermometer fell to 2° F. at Cardiff, the lowest on record there since observations began in 1904.

April 16, 1945.—An exceptionally warm day for April. It reached 81° F. in London and at Peterborough, and 83° F. at Rickmansworth.

April 4, 1946.—Temperature reached 80° F. at Greenwich, the highest so early in April for over 100 years. It was 79° F. at Mildenhall, Suffolk, and 78° F. at Woodthorpe (Notts.).

January 29, 1947.—A very low maximum temperature of 21.9° F. with brilliant sunshine was recorded at Woodthorpe, Notts. Even at Newquay it did not rise above 29° F. and in the normally very mild Scilly Isles to only 28° F.

February 24, 1947.—Extreme cold. The thermometer fell below 10° F. at many places, such as −3° F. at Luton, −2° F. at Stratford-on-Avon and Hereford, 1° F. at Coventry, Milford, Usk and Welshpool, 2° F. at Ross-on-Wye and Rye, 3° F. at Woodthorpe, Notts., 4° F. at Bath and 5° F. at Buxton.

March 1-7, 1947.—During this week extreme cold broke all previous March records at some places. Some low readings were −6° F. at Houghall and Braemar, −1° F. at Droitwich, 0° F. at Appleby, 2° F. at Shrewsbury and Buxton, 4° F. at Coventry, 5° F. Woburn, 6° F. at Hereford and Wakefield, 7° F. at Whitstable, 9° F. at York, 9½° F. at Woodthorpe, Notts., and 12° F. at Bath.

May 29-31, 1947.—Three very hot days, 90° F. in London, 88° F. at Norwich, Rugby and Lincoln, 87° F. at Birmingham, and 86° F. at Woodthorpe, Notts.

June 1-3, 1947.—Very hot. 94° F. at Waddington (Lincolnshire) and in London, 93° F. at Cambridge and Norwich, 90° F. at Leicester, Oxford and Rotherham, 89° F. at Woodthorpe, Notts. The heat was unprecedented for so early in the summer.

August 16 *and* 17, 1947.—August, 1947, was an exceptionally hot month. At Oxford the thermometer rose above 80° F. on 11 successive days. At Bournemouth 93° F. was recorded on the 16th and the same temperature at Southampton on the 16th and 17th. These were the highest temperatures ever recorded at these two places.

March 9, 1948.—Temperature exceeded 70° F. at a number of places, unprecedented warmth for so early in the year. The highest values reported were 75° F. at Wealdstone (Middlesex), 74° F. in London, Milford (Surrey), Halstead, Earls Colne (Essex), and Cromer.

July 26-30, 1948.—A spell of extreme heat. The highest temperatures reported were 95° F. at Milford (Surrey), 94° F. in London and at South Farnborough. Kew with 93° F., Blackpool 92° F., and Southport 89° F., produced new high records for July at those places. In Scotland 90° F. was touched at Prestwick, Ruthwell and Kilmarnock for the first time in July since 1911.

December 2, 1948.—New high temperature records for December in the British Isles were set up by Blacksod Point, Eire, with 64° F. and Cape Wrath 63° F.

CHAPTER XII.

SCREAMING WINDS AND RAGING SEAS

WHEN rainfall was considered it was evident that temperature played an important part in its formation. Wind, too, is most vital. Wind controls rainfall in a marked degree, and its effect on temperature is proverbial. In a word, rainfall, temperature and wind are three major factors controlling weather.

Wind is simply air in motion. Sometimes it moves so quickly it causes damage and we say a gale is blowing. On the other hand, the motion is so slight that we speak of a calm. Wind affects temperature, but what causes wind? The answer is difference of temperature. One might imagine global wind circulation in a simple way by thinking of the sun pouring down heat at the equator causing the hot air to rise. Its place would be taken by cooler air flowing in from north and south. This would in theory cause a wind to flow from the poles to the equator along the earth's surface and a return wind from the equator to the poles at some height above the ground. Actual wind circulation is by no means so simple and such a global picture is vitiated by many complicating factors.

"The wind bloweth where it listeth, and thou hearest the sound thereof, but canst not tell whence it cometh nor whither it goeth." When these words were written long years ago there were no such things as our modern weather charts. It is now known that the direction and strength of the wind are governed by natural laws. Charts will show the trajectory of the wind which is blowing, and give us quite a good knowledge of its origin and probable future course.

The British Isles lie in the track of westerly winds blowing from the Atlantic. These winds are not constant but vary considerably, being replaced at times by a reverse flow from the east. The force of the wind depends upon the barometric gradient, or perhaps we ought to say that barometric gradient depends upon the force of the wind. The barometric gradient is shown in charts by the difference in the readings of the barometer at various places measured along a line forming a radius from the centre of a depression to its perimeter. The larger the difference

TABLE V.—BEAUFORT SCALE OF WIND FORCE

No.	Description of Wind	Effects	Velocity (m.p.h.)
0	Calm	Calm ' smoke rises vertically ..	Less than 1
1	Light air ..	Direction of wind shown by smoke drift, but not by ordinary wind vanes	1—3
2	Slight breeze ..	Wind felt on face ; leaves rustle ..	4—7
3	Gentle breeze ..	Leaves and small twigs in constant motion. Wind extends light flag ..	8—12
4	Moderate breeze	Raises dust and loose paper ; small branches moved ..	13—18 13—18
5	Fresh breeze ..	Small trees in leaf sway ; wavelets on inland waters	19—24
6	Strong breeze ..	Large branches in motion ; telegraph wires whistle ; umbrellas used with difficulty	25—31
7	High wind ..	Whole trees in motion; inconvenience when walking against wind ..	32—38
8	Gale	Breaks twigs off trees ; generally impedes progress	39—46
9	Strong gale ..	Slight structural damage (chimney pots and slates)	47—54
10	Whole gale ..	Seldom felt inland ; trees uprooted ; considerable structural damage ..	55—63
11	Storm ..	Very rare ; widespread damage ..	64—75
12	Hurricane ..	.. ..	Above 75

(or steeper the gradient) the stronger will be the wind. If isobaric lines on a chart are near together winds will be strong, if far apart, winds will be light. Winds are light in an anticyclone, except sometimes near the edge in territory forming a no-man's land between an anticyclone and a depression.

Have you seen headlines in the press like "Eighty mile an hour gale sweeps England. Widespread damage," or "Ninety miles an hour gale in the Channel. Ships struggle with mountainous seas"? Fortunately for us all there was not an eighty or ninety mile an hour wind careering across Britain or the Channel.

A gale is officially described as a wind blowing at more than 38 miles per hour. A wind of 45 miles per hour over England, or 55 m.p.h. over the Channel, is quite severe. Most people would call a thirty mile an hour wind a gale. It is not suggested that journalists write fairy stories about the wind. The figures they often quote are those for severe gusts. The land surface, with its many irregularities and buildings, considerably affects the structure of a strong wind. Not only has the land surface a powerful braking effect, but gives the wind its characteristic

TABLE VI.—FACTS ABOUT WIND

	Days with GALES in Year	Hours with GALES in Year	Days with STRONG WINDS in Year	Hours with STRONG WINDS in Year	Average Highest Hourly Wind m.p.h.	Average Highest Gust m.p.h.
SCOTLAND						
Lerwick ..	41	255	178	1740	57	87
Stornaway ..	54	230	198	1880	58	87
Tiree ..	20	105	139	1308	54	83
Paisley ..	0.4	0.6	20	75	36	76
Bell Rock ..	49	275	205	1890	60	85
Edinburgh ..	7	22	68	415	47	75
ISLE OF MAN						
Pt. of Ayre ..	20	106	146	1243	51	78
ENGLAND						
South Shields ..	4	15	58	344	44	71
Spurn Head ..	12	50	125	960	50	72
Fleetwood ..	11	76	93	670	54	77
Liverpool ..	9	49	74	600	50	82
Holyhead ..	17	90	133	1070	54	80
Cranwell ..	1	3	39	200	40	68
Birmingham ..	0.3	0.5	21	83	37	68
Kew	0	0	13	55	32	61
Dover ..	4	16	77	533	43	65
Plymouth ..	13	48	75	500	52	71
Scilly Isles ..	27	146	164	1670	58	86
EIRE						
Kingstown ..	15	63	150	1060	55	?

gusts and lulls. Over the sea the wind blows more strongly and evenly than over the land.

In 1805, Admiral Sir Francis Beaufort devised a wind scale which bears his name, and is still used for making approximate non-instrumental estimates of the force of the wind. An extract from this scale is given, and an amateur, with a little practice, can make wind estimates of fair accuracy.

As our worst gales blow from the south-west and west it is not surprising that the western seaboard is more subject to gales than other districts. Gales are less frequent on the East Coast, particularly from Flamborough Head to the Thames Estuary. Here the average number of days with gales in a year is 18, compared with 36 on our West Coast.

Instrumental records of wind velocity are kept at a number of places, and these show that the Hebrides, the Shetlands, and the Scilly Isles are especially subject to great winds. The isolated Bell Rock Lighthouse, East of Fife, is also very windswept.

Table VI. is given for reference; it gives interesting facts for selected situations in the British Isles.

At Bell Rock and Stornoway the wind is strong or gale force for an average of about six hours per day over the year, or three months of strong wind out of twelve. In the Scillies, strong winds blow on an average five hours a day. At the other extreme, Kew has strong winds only for an average of nine minutes a day, or rather more than half per cent. of the year, while the chances of a gale are so small that the average is given as nil. Other inland places, such as Cranwell and Birmingham, also have the characteristic small incidence of strong winds. Indeed, compared with what happens on exposed parts of our West Coast and over the open sea, dwellers in inland districts hardly know what wind is.

Even at exposed places it is unusual for a gale of more than 60 miles an hour to occur. The highest velocity on record is 78 miles an hour at Fleetwood on December 22, 1894. Occasionally in very severe gales gusts of 100 miles an hour are recorded. The fiercest gusts on record are 113 miles an hour at St. Ann's Head, Pembroke, on January 18, 1945, and 111 miles per hour at Scilly on December 6, 1929. Exactly the same value was reported from Quilty, Eire, on January 27, 1920, but there is just a slight uncertainty about this. Other tremendous gusts known to have occurred are 108 m.p.h. at Tiree (Hebrides) on January 28, 1927; 107 m.p.h. at Holyhead on February 28, 1937; 104 m.p.h. at Paisley on January 28, 1927; 101 m.p.h. at Bell Rock on October 19, 1935, and Liverpool on January 29, 1938. In the Isle of Man an anemometer was not installed until 1936, but a gust of 90 m.p.h. was registered at the Point of Ayre on December 6, 1936. At Kew the strongest gust was 73 m.p.h. on November 23, 1938.

It might be assumed that a wind blowing at 60 miles an hour was twice as strong as one of 30 m.p.h. This is not so. A wind of 35 m.p.h. exerts a pressure of 3.6 lbs. to the square foot, or about three times the pressure of a 20 mile an hour wind. A wind of 50 miles an hour exerts a pressure of 7.7 lbs. per square foot, or more than twice that of a 35 m.p.h. wind. It will be seen, therefore, how disastrous these high velocities can be if they occur on land.

Temperature and Wind.

"The North wind doth blow and we shall have snow." "When the wind is in the East, 'Tis good for neither man nor beast." "When ye see the South wind blow ye say there shall be heat, and it cometh to pass." "Out of the South cometh the whirl-wind."

These are one or two of the many sayings about wind, and there is much truth about them. Everyone knows that in winter a south-west wind setting in in time of frost heralds a thaw; everyone knows, too, that a north-east wind in winter or spring is cold. In summer a south-west wind is warm unless conditions are rainy. In fact, wind direction affects temperature very considerably, especially in winter when the sun's rays are weak. Let us make a tour of the compass.

A south wind in winter is usually transitory in front of a depression. It is rather mild. In summer this wind often brings heat, but it is frequently of the humid thundery type. Visibility is not good, as a rule. Even in summer this wind often causes enough haze to blot out distant objects.

The south-west wind is the mildest winter wind. In summer it is warm unless conditions are unsettled. It often feels close owing to the humidity.

A west wind is cooler than the south-west, especially in winter. The atmosphere is clearer and drier than with south and south-west winds.

The north-west wind is cool at all seasons. There may be frost in winter. It is dry and visibility good.

A north wind is cold in winter and spring, and cool in summer. It is dry and visibility is often excellent.

Winds from the north-east are cold in winter and spring, but heavy rain may fall with this wind if a depression is moving up the English Channel or across Southern England.

East winds are very cold in winter and spring with a characteristic dry harshness. In summer they are warm over England but relatively cool on the East Coast.

A south-east wind often heralds a rise in temperature in winter. In summer, great heat may come from the Continent with this wind.

These are general effects, but Britain has such geographical diversities that special places have their own features. At Lowestoft, for example, a south wind would come from the sea and be cooler than a south wind at Norwich. A south wind in summer would be cooler at Ramsgate than at Margate. Observe the position of Penzance. Winds from south-east, south, south-west, west, north-west and north are all sea winds or sea winds slightly modified by passing over a few miles of land. The only real land winds are those from north-east and east-north-east. The highest temperature in summer would occur with these two winds, provided England was having a warm spell. At Southport the warmest summer winds will be south-east and south. During a hot spell over England winds from south-east, south, and south-west would be relatively cool at Brighton or Eastbourne compared with the same winds twenty miles inland.

The relation between wind direction and maximum temperature was calculated for Nottingham for each month over a period of twenty years. Figure 30 shows the results for February and August. In February the coldest winds were north-east and east with average maxima of 40° F. and 37° F., compared with

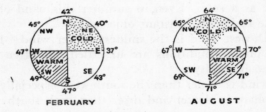

FIG. 30. RELATION BETWEEN TEMPERATURE AND
WIND DIRECTION AT NOTTINGHAM.

47° F. for west and south winds, and 49° F. for south-west winds. In August, south-east and south winds averaged 71° F., while the north wind was 7° F. cooler at 64° F.

It is a common belief that east winds are always cold, but this is only true in winter and spring. In the Midlands it is a warm dry wind in summer. The temperature of the east wind in England is largely controlled by temperatures prevailing on the Continent. The North Sea cools the east wind in summer, but warms it in winter. If the wind blew continuously from the east all the year round, England would have long severe winters and hot summers, with short springs and autumns. In the Isle of Man the people fear the north-west wind more than the east, for the latter has been robbed of some of its venom in its passage across the Irish Sea.

Wind may be deflected. A south wind on the Atlantic may be bent to blow as a west wind over Britain with a south wind character. When a wind has characteristics strange to its direction, it is probably a deflected wind.

The Sea and the Wind.

The state of the sea depends upon the force and direction of the wind. It may be anything from pond-like to a roaring tumble of huge waves. The stronger the wind the greater the waves. Near the coast the sea may be calm with a stiff breeze blowing, if the wind is blowing from the land, but a wind blowing inshore brings the breakers. A high south-west wind will make it rough in the Channel, but just round the corner of the South Foreland, near Deal, it would be calm enough for ships to shelter. In a north-east gale the sea off Deal would be heavy, but near the Sussex coast would be almost calm. There are sandbanks off the East Coast south of the Humber. These help to break the waves so that the water inshore does not become so rough as it otherwise would. Ships can thus shelter off Yarmouth in an east wind. Anyone who has experienced storms in the North Sea and off Land's End will know that the waves in the two areas differ considerably in type. The cliffs at the toe of England are open to the pounding of the mighty Atlantic rollers. Sometimes when it is comparatively calm one may find a huge swell with waves twenty feet in height from trough to crest, but the wave length (or distance between the crests) is great. Such a sea is like smooth rolling country. The North Sea is much more shallow. As a consequence, the waves are much shorter from crest to crest. This means steeper waves and a more confused sea. Sailors accustomed to the North Sea do not like our western coasts, and Welsh and West Country sailors dislike the North Sea.

Whether the storm is in the North Sea, the English Channel, or out by the Scillies, the raging turmoil of angry water seen from the deck of a ship is a majestic, inspiring spectacle. The huge waves and the thunderous roar, mingled with the screaming and screeching of the wind as it tears across a ship has to be seen and heard to be credited.

G

The air holds invisible moisture even on the driest days, just as water can hold dissolved invisible salt. If two mercury thermometers are mounted side by side, with the bulb of one of them covered in muslin which is kept moist by water from a small container, we can tell the amount of moisture in the air. Such an instrument is called a hygrometer. Water evaporates from the wet bulb, and as evaporation causes cooling, this chills the mercury. The drier the air the more rapid the evaporation, and hence the greater the difference between the two thermometers. Tables are available from which (knowing the readings of the wet and dry bulbs) we can learn the relative humidity and dew-point.

There are two kinds of humidity, relative and absolute. It is the former we hear most about in meteorology. Relative humidity is read on a scale of 0 to 100, 0 being absolute dryness and 100 saturation. A relative humidity of 80 means that the air contains 80 per cent. of the moisture it can hold at the prevailing temperature. Absolute dryness does not occur in nature, though instances have occurred in the Sahara Desert of values as low as 2 or 4 per cent. Relative humidity is greatest over the British Isles in December and January, varying little over the country at that season, the afternoon average being about 85 per cent. at most places. It is lowest in spring and early summer. At this season the air is driest in the South Midlands with an average of about 60 per cent., compared with 75 to 80 per cent. round the coasts. Humidity is highest on the coasts owing to the presence of the sea, and lowest inland. At Kew on a summer afternoon the average is about 59 per cent., but 72 per cent. at Aberdeen and Falmouth. In the small islands of Scilly humidity on a summer afternoon is 81 per cent., only slightly less than in January.

Relative humidity varies greatly in the course of a day. It is highest when the temperature is lowest, and least in the warmth of the afternoon. At Kew, in January, it varies from 86 per cent. at 5 a.m. to 80 per cent. at 1 p.m., and in July from 87 per cent.

at 5 a.m. to 60 per cent. at 1 p.m.   On clear, calm nights inland
the air falls to about dew-point, which means about 100 per cent.
relative humidity.   Cloudy nights (because the temperature does
not fall so much) have drier air than clear ones.   When the air
is damp and mild it has a characteristic muggy feeling.
Occasionally, the relative humidity inland falls to 20 or 30 per
cent.   Record low values occurred in 1942, when on April 15th
at 3.15 G.M.T. Kew reported a humidity as low as 10 per cent.
On May 6th 9 per cent. was observed at Woodthorpe, Notts.
Such a Saharan atmosphere is indeed rare in Britain.

Absolute humidity is the actual, not the relative, amount of
moisture in the air.   It is least in winter and highest in summer.
This may seem strange at first sight, but warm air can contain
much more moisture than cold air without visible sign.   A January day with a temperature of 30° F. and saturated air would
only contain, volume for volume, a little more than one-third
of the moisture of an ordinary July day with a temperature of
70 °F., and a relative humidity of 60 per cent.   This is the secret
of the torrential thunder rains of summer.

A "Drying Day."

Housewives on "wash-day" like a good "drying day."   What
conditions dry clothes most quickly?   There are four factors:
humidity, temperature, wind and sunshine.   The best drying day
is a warm one with a low humidity, plenty of sunshine and a
good breeze.   Conversely, the worst conditions for drying are
high humidity, cold air, overcast sky and calm air.   If the temperature is below freezing clothes will become stiff, but if left
some time outside they will soften and will be found nearly dry.
Why?   The moisture in them becomes ice, but even ice evaporates, though more slowly than water.

Humidity Indoors.

On a warm day in summer the relative humidity in a
laboratory was found to be higher than in winter.   Why?
Assume the outdoor temperature to be 40° F. and relative
humidity 85 per cent.   Humidity tables would show the vapour
pressure to be 7.1 millibars.   If the laboratory is heated to 60° F.
and the air for ventilation drawn from outside, the humidity
tables would show that the relative humidity in the laboratory
should be about 40 per cent.   On a warm summer day the out-

side temperature might be 80° F. with a relative humidity of 50 per cent., giving a vapour pressure of 17.5 millibars. Inside the laboratory the temperature would be lower, probably about 70° F., and a temperature of 70° F. with a vapour pressure of 17.5 millibars means a relative humidity of 70 per cent. So the reason for the higher humidity indoors in summer becomes apparent. In a house the kitchens and bathrooms would have a higher relative humidity than the other rooms.

Dew.

Whatever the poets may say, dew does not fall. It forms on the surface where it is seen. The process is the same as that which causes steaming windows. Dew forms when the temperature falls considerably on still clear nights. It is thus to some extent a sign of fine weather. A heavy dew, however, may indicate increasing moisture and approaching unsettled weather. Wind and cloud, by checking nocturnal radiation prevent, or lessen, the formation of dew.

Hoar Frost.

Hoar is not just frozen dew. It is a covering of ice crystals which have formed on the grass and other objects. A thick hoar-frost, particularly when a bright sun shines on it, is an entrancing sight. There is an impression which is common that a thick hoar means a severe frost. This is not so. The thickness or otherwise of the hoar depends on the humidity. Some of our most severe frosts have little hoar, and we call them black frosts. In spring and autumn hoar-frost may form, sometimes profusely, when the temperature in the screen does not fall lower than 34° F. or 35° F.

Fog.

Fog is one of the most unpleasant items in our weather programme, and can paralyse road traffic. The air may be saturated without fog forming, and muggy weather is not often associated with fog of much density. Yet fog is allied to humidity, for it is a kind of cloud resting on the earth's surface. Clear, calm weather is necessary for its formation, and fogs are most frequent in autumn and winter. The type of weather which favours fogs in winter (anticyclonic) is the same that often gives us brilliant weather in summer. Indeed, blue sky usually

exists above thick fog, and a foggy day in one district may
prevail, while there is continuous sunshine a short distance away.
Fog forms most readily where temperature falls most quickly in
the evening, that is, in inland valleys. This fact has led many
people to assume that valley fog is due to damp rising from the
valley stream or river. This is quite untrue. Were there no
river the valley would still have its fog. Do not assume that a
place subject to thick fogs is necessarily damp. The fog may
actually be accentuated by a place's dryness. This may sound
absurd, but in a dry locality nocturnal radiation is stronger and
the temperature falls more quickly to a point favourable to fog
formation. A damp place may retard the night's fall in temperature and in this way really hinder fog formation. Nottingham is subject to fogs, sometimes of great density, and the dry
sandstone of the district is doubtless a factor in increasing their
frequency and density. A fog may be dense yet quite shallow.
The author lives on a slope thirty feet above the floor of a valley
and two hundred feet below the crest of the flanking hills. He
has seen dense fog so shallow that from an upstairs window the
hill top nearly a mile away could be plainly observed in clear
sunshine, while the garden lawn twenty feet or so below the
window was quite blotted out by fog looking like a mass of cotton-
wool.

In and near large towns fogs are vitiated by smoke from
thousands of chimneys. It is dark or yellowish and irritates
the breathing passages. In most towns it is not so much the
factory chimneys which are to blame, but the ordinary domestic
chimney. The smoke rising from a few factory chimneys is
visually impressive, but it is the aggregated effects of the trickles
of smoke from thousands of house chimneys which cause the
main pollution.

It is very important for us to have clean air to breathe. We
already have clean drinking water; when shall we insist on clean
air? Our women ought to be interested in this matter, for it is
they who have much extra unnecessary work in the home as a
direct result of dirty air. Radiation fogs cannot be abolished,
but they could be made very much cleaner.

What constitutes a fog? We can look out of the window
and say it is foggy or misty, but what is the rule? One could
imagine an observer in, say Llandudno or the Isle of Man, speak-
ing of "fog" on a day which a dweller in an English manufac-

TABLE VII.—FACTS ABOUT VISIBILITY

	Dense Fog	Fog	Mist or Poor Visibility	Moderate Visibility	Good Visibility
	days	days	days	days	days
Scotland					
Lerwick	0	8	11	54	292
Stornoway ..	0	2	12	67	284
Tiree	0	3	8	53	301
Aberdeen ..	0.2	9	28	109	219
Braemar ..	0	3	70	115	177
Edinburgh ..	0.2	25	83	195	62
Renfrew ..	1	28	77	95	165
Isle of Man					
Douglas	0	9	18	115	223
Pt. of Ayre ..	0	5	4	24	332
England					
Tynemouth ..	0.3	20	37	148	160
Harrogate ..	0.5	41	89	39	196
Manchester ..	8	55	113	118	79
Cranwell ..	0.3	41	58	146	120
Nottingham ..	4	81	109	124	51
Birmingham ..	1	36	99	85	145
Yarmouth ..	1	16	32	212	105
Ross-on-Wye ..	0.2	31	52	78	204
Oxford	1	29	46	114	176
Kew	2	35	100	120	110
Brighton ..	0.1	12	60	148	145
Plymouth ..	0.2	7	25	91	242
Falmouth ..	4	11	3	68	283
The Lizard ..	1	22	13	27	303
Newquay ..	0	6	27	70	262
Scilly Isles ..	0.3	17	14	62	272
Guernsey ..	0.2	11	38	84	232
Wales					
Llandudno ..	0	2	18	35	310
Eire					
Birr Castle ..	0	12	8	40	305
Markree ..	0.3	7	18	74	266
Valentia	0	2	9	48	306
Northern Ireland					
Armagh	0.1	8	20	52	285

turing town would simply call hazy. There is a story that a native observer in the clear air of the Egyptian Sudan once entered in his record, "Visibility poor, limit of vision twelve miles."

In order to standardise fog observations an international code was formulated some years ago. In this code it is "foggy" whenever the limit of visibility is less than 1,100 yards (1,000 metres). If one cannot see 55 yards it is classed as dense. Visibility exceeding 1¼ miles but not more than 2½ miles is "poor." Good visibility is the condition when objects over 6¼ miles away can be seen.

Industrial districts in the Midlands, East Lancashire, West Yorkshire, and the Clyde Valley round Glasgow have a high incidence of fog. Coastal areas have least fog.

The following Table is given for reference to show the average state of visibility at a number of places over a period of years.

Sea Fog.

Fog at sea is due to different causes from land fog. The latter, as we have seen, is due to rapid chilling of the air on clear still nights. Sea fog is produced, as a rule, by warm air blowing over a cool water surface, so that the warm air is chilled below dew-point. This process is most likely to occur in late spring and early summer, and least likely in winter. On land the reverse is the case, high incidence of fog in autumn and winter, and low incidence in spring and summer. Warm, sub-tropical air blowing up the cool English Channel is a source of sea fog. Fog is most frequent in the English Channel in April, May and June, and least so from September to December.

Most seamen dread fog more than a gale.

The fog often experienced in river estuaries, such as the Clyde, the Humber and the Thames, is not sea fog proper, but land fog which has drifted over the comparatively narrow stretch of water. The mouth of the Seine in France is also liable to this fog.

Occasionally, after severe frost, a warm south-west wind blowing over snow-covered ground may cause fog in the same manner as at sea. This occurred in the English Midlands on January 7, 1940.

CHAPTER XIV.

"We Shall Have Snow"

Over the lowlands of Britain snow is not much more than a passing visitor, though three recent winters beginning with 1939-40 have been exceptionally snowy. In mountainous districts snow may lie for weeks or even months at a time, but such areas are almost devoid of population. In the lowlands it is very unusual for a winter to pass without some snow. As the old lady remarked: "I've noticed for fifty years we either get snow before or after Christmas."

Snow falls when the temperature is low, but if the thermometer is a few degrees above freezing point it is usually called sleet. It is not frozen rain. More snow falls after Christmas than before. At the autumnal equinox it is very rare, but it is quite common in March.

Most of our snow falls in the three months January to March. At Kew, for example, with 13 snow days per annum the first three months of the year account for nine of them.

On Ben Nevis snow falls on an average on 170 days a year, and in 1885 there were 206 days with snow. The Scilly Isles are almost snowless and so is the toe of Cornwall.

Table VIII. gives interesting facts about snowfall, showing the average number of days on which snow falls in a year, and the number on which it lies on the ground. The height above sea-level is given because this is an important factor in snowfall.

It is interesting to observe that snow does not often lie in the Hebrides and on the West Coast of Scotland. While snow is frequent in the Shetlands, at Wick and at Banff, the number of days on which it lies is comparatively small. Contrast Lerwick, with 39 snow days and 8 days snow lying, with York, which has 15 snow days, but 12 snow lying. Huddersfield has two points of observation and is a good example of the effect that can ensue with only 400 feet difference in height.

In the London area the average for five points was calculated over six years. Hampstead shows the influence of height, but the effect of a large built-up area is also seen. A great city with its million or more domestic fires and heated buildings can

TABLE VIII.—FACTS ABOUT SNOWFALL

			Height above Sea Level	Days with Snow	Days with Snow Lying
SCOTLAND			feet		
Lerwick	..	..	269	39	8
Stornoway	..	..	79	24	4
Tiree	..	..	24	10	1
Wick	..	..	81	36	10
Banff	..	..	130	29	6
Aberdeen	..	..	79	34	15
Braemar	..	..	1111	41	60
Dalwhinnie	..	..	1176	57	64
Perth	..	..	76	20	8
Edinburgh	..	..	190	13	5
Oban	..	..	229	14	3
Rothesay	..	..	200	14	4
ISLE OF MAN					
Douglas	..	..	284	15	4
ENGLAND					
Durham	..	..	336	20	16
Scarborough	..	..	118	14	7
York	..	..	57	15	12
Hull	..	..	8	21	7
Harrogate	..	..	478	24	21
Huddersfield (Oakes)	..	761	30	24
Huddersfield	..	..	325	19	18
Manchester	..	..	125	17	5
Southport	..	..	35	11	4
Buxton	..	..	1007	29	21
Nottingham	..	..	170	23	14
Birmingham	..	..	425	23	10
Skegness	..	..	15	15	7
Cromer	..	..	178	16	5
Norwich	..	..	110	17	12
Yarmouth	..	..	5	17	4
Felixstowe	..	..	15	15	6
Cambridge	..	..	41	11	6
Shoeburyness	..	..	11	14	4
Oxford	..	..	208	18	6
Tunbridge Wells	..	..	351	13	6
Eastbourne	..	..	35	6	2
Brighton	..	..	32	7	2
Ventnor	..	..	60	7	2
Shaftesbury	..	..	722	10	8
Cheltenham	..	..	214	13	6
Bath	..	..	67	9	4
Cullompton	..	..	202	6	3
Torquay	..	..	27	5	1
Plymouth	..	..	82	7	1
Falmouth	..	..	167	5	0.6
Newquay	..	..	182	1	0.2
Scilly Isles	..	..	163	3	0.2

TABLE VIII.—FACTS ABOUT SNOWFALL—*continued*

		Height above Sea Level	Days with Snow	Days with Snow Lying
LONDON AREA				
Average for 6 years		feet		
Hampstead	.. ..	450	21	10
Enfield	.. ..	148	13	5
Kew	.. ..	18	15	3
Regent's Park	.. ..	129	11	3
Westminster	.. ..	27	9	1
Jersey	.. .. ..	28	3	2
WALES				
Holyhead	.. ..	26	7	2
Llandudno	.. ..	13	8	1
Swansea ..	.. ..	33	4	1
NORTHERN IRELAND				
Armagh ..	.. ..	204	15	8
EIRE				
Dublin ..	.. ..	155	13	4
Birr Castle	.. ..	173	10	2
Waterford	.. ..	137	3	2
Valentia ..	.. ..	30	5	0.4

produce sufficient artificial heat to turn snow into sleet or rain in its centre. Most of our snow falls with the thermometer near freezing point so that a change of a degree or two in temperature decides whether it lies or not. There must be numbers of occasions in our large cities when snow thaws as it falls, but lies unthawed in surrounding rural districts.

An attempt was made at Nottingham in the winter of 1938-39 to contrast depths of snow lying in the city and outskirts at different altitudes. On January 5, 1939, snow lay 8½ inches deep on Ramsdale Hill (500 feet), 5¼ inches at Woodthorpe (225 feet), 3 inches in the Market Square (centre of city at 120 feet) and 4¼ inches in the suburb of West Bridgford (80 feet). Two days later the depths of snow lying were: Ramsdale Hill 7 inches, Woodthorpe 3¾ inches, and West Bridgford 1¾ inches. On January 26, 1939, Ramsdale Hill had 4½ inches, Woodthorpe 1½ inches, but the Market Square and West Bridgford had no snow.

The tradition of a snowy Christmas as seasonable is legendary, with little basis in fact. At Kew, snow falls on an average on two days in December, so that assuming that the probable incidence of snow is constant through the month only one year in five would have snow on Christmas Eve, or Christmas Day, or on Boxing Day. At Nottingham, of the 29 Christmasses from 1915-1943 snow was lying on Christmas Day on only five occasions, 1916, 1923, 1925, 1927 and 1938.

Professor K. C. Edwards, M.A., Ph.D., of Nottingham University, suggests that the tradition of snow at Christmas may have originated from the snow scene on Christmas cards. The custom of sending these cards seems to have come to us from Central Europe, where a snow-clad countryside would be much more common at Christmas, particularly in the upland forest regions.

One hears the expression on a winter day, "If it snows it will lie, because the ground is dry." This is not necessarily true. It is the temperature which decides whether or not snow will lie. If the temperature is 35° F. or 36° F. snow will thaw as it falls, no matter how dry the ground. On the other hand, if it is raining and a change of wind brings snow and a fall in temperature to 30° F., the snow will begin to lie on the wet ground, at first as slush, and finally as dry snow.

In winter snow will lie drier on a day of clear blue sky than on a cloudy one. The reason is that with a clear sky, ground temperature will be low and the small angle of the sun's rays means small heating power. On such a day the thermometer in the screen may rise to 38° F. with no sign of thaw, especially if the air is dry. If the temperature of the wet bulb of the hygrometer is below freezing any tendency for the snow to thaw would be checked by the cold of evaporation keeping it below 32° F. On a cloudy day with a high humidity the ground temperature would be little, if any, below that of the screen, and snow would soften at 33° F., and become slush at 35° F.

"It's too cold to snow." Most of us have heard this remark. Is it true? It is never too cold, and in Canada and the polar regions snow falls with a temperature below zero. It is true, however, that the colder the air the less moisture it can contain, and so very cold air is not the potential reservoir for a fall of snow that air at 30° F. would be. Probably little snow falls in these islands at a temperature of 20° F. or less.

London is more free from really heavy snow than any other large city in Britain, and a great proportion of our population who live in large towns are quite unaware of the tremendous snowfalls which take place on high land.

High altitude roads such as those which cross the Pennines from Durham to Cumberland, and from Derbyshire to Cheshire, have fifteen feet high snow posts to indicate the roadway in snowy weather. Sometimes even these are buried in drifts. In Sutherland, railway lines are protected at exposed points by wooden sheds, otherwise dry snow blowing from the vast moorlands would pile up in great drifts on the track.

We have learnt that the West of Britain has milder winters and less frost than the centre and East. It might reasonably be supposed then that less snow falls in the West. In general, this is true. There are periods, however, when a cold current of air covers the whole country. When this happens snow may fall in greater quantity in the West, because the air there affords a greater reservoir for moisture. This occurred during the great frosts of 1895, 1917 and 1929.

It used to be assumed that some of the snow-fields of the Cairngorms were perennial, and not without good reason, because observations had been kept on them for half a century and they had never completely disappeared. In September, 1933, after a very warm summer, these supposedly eternal patches of snow disappeared, and it must now be admitted that there is no perpetual snow in Scotland. Nevertheless, it can be said that it is very rare for this snow to melt entirely away in the summer, and if it does the period between its disappearance and the arrival of new autumn snow will be very brief. On the summits of high mountains the wind is so strong that snow cannot lie to great depths, as it is blown away in great clouds and scattered over the lower slopes and valleys.

Were it not for this fact it is quite possible that small glaciers would exist in the Grampian Mountains.

The following facts relating to days with snow-cover on high land are from calculations made by G. Manley, M.A., M.Sc., of Cambridge.

		Snow lying
At 3,000 feet in the Snowdon area	108 days per annum
At 3,000 feet in the Lake District	135 days per annum
At 3,000 feet in Cairngorms	165 days per annum
Bodmin Moor at 1,000 feet	6 to 8 days
Leith Hill at 900 feet	18 days
North Chilterns at 700 feet	21 days
Lammermuirs at 1,500 feet	72 to 75 days
Caithness Hills at 1,500 feet	110 days
Snaefell, I.O.M., at 1,500 feet	25 days

Some of our main roads touch great heights in places and are liable to be seriously affected by snow. The following may be mentioned, and the snow-cover estimates are also by Mr. G. Manley. On the Scottish Border, 10 miles south of Jedburgh at Carter Bar, the London to Edinburgh road reaches a height of 1,300 feet. It is liable to be snow-covered at this point on 53 days in the year. On the London to Glasgow road, about ten miles south of Penrith, there is the well-known Shap, where the road is over 1,300 feet; this is liable to snow-cover on 40 days. The road over the North Pennines from Scotch Corner to Appleby reaches a height of 1,400 feet passing over Stainmore. Snow-cover may be expected on 50 days. Travelling from Sheffield to Manchester through Glossop, a height of 1,500 feet is touched at the "Snake," in the Peak District, where snow is probable on 45 days. Perhaps the most impressive of our main roads is that from Perth to Braemar, where at Cairnwell, near the famous "Devil's Elbow," about ten miles south of Braemar, the 2,000 feet line is reached with a snow-cover probability of 120 days, or a third of the year. Two other points may be mentioned, Drumochter 1,500 feet on the Perth-Inverness road (about five miles south of Dalwhinnie) with 75 days of snow-cover, and Rannoch Moor, 1,100 feet, on the Glencoe Road, where snow lies on about 55 days.

CHAPTER XV.

—And What May Happen if We Do

This chapter is made up of brief notes in the form of a diary on some of the more striking falls of snow which have occurred over our islands in the past eighty years.

October 19, 1880.—Six inches of snow fell in London area, a remarkably heavy fall for October.

January 18-21, 1881.—One of the greatest snowstorms on record in Southern England. Most of England south of the Wash had more than six inches. Twelve inches lay over Southern England from Sussex to the borders of Cornwall. In Brighton, average depth was 18 inches. In Exeter there were 12 to 14 inches; Kingsbridge (Devon) 18 inches; Cullompton 22 inches; and Sherborne (Dorset) 24 inches. A depression moved from the Bay of Biscay to the Isle of Wight, turned south to France, then moved east-north-east. England was thus in the cold sector of the system. Three to four feet of snow fell on Dartmoor.

December 4-8, 1882.—This storm centred over Northern England and South Scotland, and is known as the Border Blizzard. It was one of the worst storms in our annals. It gave three to four feet of undrifted snow, but most of it fell in wild, thinly populated country.

June 10, 1888.—Six inches of snow are said to have fallen in parts of Scotland.

July 11, 1888.—A light fall of snow occurred with a bleak northerly wind over most of the British Isles. It is almost the only authenticated fall of snow in July in the lowlands.

March 9-13, 1891.—A great blizzard in Southern England. In Devon and Cornwall the average depth was two feet, with immense drifts. The express train which left Paddington at 3 p.m. on Monday, March 9th, got as far as Brent on a southern spur of Dartmoor, where it ran into a huge drift and was imprisoned for four days, eventually reaching Plymouth at 8.30 p.m. on Friday, March 13th. Three or four feet fell on Dartmoor. The track of the depression causing this storm was from the Bay of Biscay, north-eastwards up the English Channel.

May 18, 1891.—Round this date snow fell in the Midlands and East Anglia to a depth of six inches.

February, 1895.—A heavy snowstorm in the first half of this month in South-West Scotland, North-West England and the Isle of Man brought traffic to a standstill. Depth in Galloway 2½ feet.

February, 1900.—A very snowy spell in the first half of the month gave a foot of snow lying over most of the British Isles.

December, 1906.—A heavy snowfall was general in Christmas week; very severe in East Scotland.

January 29, 1907.—A blizzard with thunder and lightning at Huddersfield produced eight inches of snow in about two hours, with drifts of five feet.

April 23-25, 1908.—On April 23rd a foot of snow lay in parts of Norfolk and Suffolk. On 24th, six inches lay at Epsom. On 25th, Southampton reported 14 inches, and Totland Bay, Isle of Wight, 10 inches. On April 26th, there were 11 inches at Marlborough, 16 inches at Oxford, and as much as 19 inches at Bucklebury.

March, 1909.—In the opening days of this month Kent and South-East England had heavy snow approaching two feet in places. At Walthamstow 8 inches lay on the evening of March 3rd.

January 11-12, 1913.—One of the most severe easterly blizzards in half a century in South Scotland and North England. Numerous places had about two and a half feet of snow.

February 24, 1916.—Twelve inches of snow fell at Nottingham.

March, 1916.—A very snowy month in the Pennines. At Wearhead, Durham, it was reported that "a continuous blizzard prevailed right through the month." Something like 10 feet of snow fell in the Pennines. The High Peak railway, Derbyshire, was unworkable for some time.

January 16, 1917.—Five inches of snow fell at Newquay, the heaviest fall on record there in half a century.

April, 1917.—A great blizzard on the Scottish Border.

May, 1923.—In this bleak month a snowstorm raged almost without pause in the Cairngorms, where conditions at 4,000 feet suggested Spitzbergen at sea-level.

October 28, 1926.—Twelve inches of snow fell at Dalnaspidal.

December 25-27, 1927.—A depression from the Atlantic moved south-west from Eire to the English Channel and across France to the Mediterranean. It caused a great snowstorm in Southern England. About 6 p.m. on Christmas Day rain in the south turned to snow so heavy that roads were hopelessly blocked by midnight. Even in London, traffic was difficult. The storm raged all the 26th. Half a foot of snow lay in Central London. On Salisbury Plain the drifts were 20 feet deep. At Princetown, Dartmoor, many houses had snow up to the bedroom windows. Outside London many cars stuck fast and were even buried. In Devon, Thurlestone, Hallsands and Bigbury were isolated. Salcombe could only communicate with the outer world by sea. Snowdrifts on Dartmoor reached 30 feet. A very impressive sight were the clouds of snow blowing out to sea from the cliffs of Devon, Dorset and the Isle of Wight, which seamen on passing ships thought to be fog. St. Albans was isolated for several days. An interesting little book dealing with this storm is "The Great Blizzard of Christmas, 1927," by the Rev. H. Hugh Breton, M.A., F.R.Met.S.

February 16, 1929.—A small tract on the south-east fringe of Dartmoor to the west of Holne Chase, had six feet of snow in 15 hours without any drifting. It was like a cloudburst of snow. Eye witnesses describe it as coming down as though shovelled. This was probably the deepest fall of snow ever measured in a single day's storm in the British Isles at as low an elevation as 1,000 feet. (See L. C. W. Bonacina in "British Rainfall, 1936.")

February 23-26, 1933.—A depression moved southwards over Eire drawing in supplies of damp Atlantic air whilst maintaining a bitterly cold easterly surface wind over most of the British Isles. A great snowstorm ensued. At Harrogate 30 inches fell in three days and roads over the Pennines were impassable. The average depth of snow at Huddersfield on the evening of the 26th, was 30 inches, which was stated to be the greatest within living memory. At Buxton 29 inches lay. The train Royal Scot arrived at Euston over twelve hours late. At Whipsnade two feet of snow fell, but London, only 40 miles away, had a mere two inches.

February, 1934.—At the end of the month, Hull and Holderness had from one to two feet of snow.

October 31, 1934.—A cold northerly current brought snow to many places. Two inches fell as far south as Belvoir Castle.

March 11, 1935.—Four and a half to six inches of snow lying at Newton Abbot, Devon.

May 17, 1935.—There was a very cold spell from May 12th to 17th. Places as far apart as Harrogate and Tiverton, Devon reported five inches of snow on the 17th. In the Pennine dales from two to three feet were said to have fallen.

January 22, 1936.—Snow 18 inches deep at Buxton.

February 27-28, 1937.—A severe snowstorm swept Scotland, North England and Wales. Roads were blocked and trees and telegraph poles damaged. On the 28th, 14 inches of undrifted snow lay at Macclesfield and 24 inches at Buxton.

March 11-14, 1937.—A severe snowstorm in South Scotland, North England and Northern Ireland. Practically all roads were impassable to wheeled traffic in Ulster.

December 7, 1937. — Heavy snow in the South. Two feet at Shaftesbury on 8th and 9th.

December 11, 1937.—Eleven inches of snow at Durham.

January 26, 1939.—Nineteen inches of snow at Stanford Dingley, Berks.

January, 1940.—This very severe month had some great snowfalls. On 17th, one foot lay at Eastbourne. On 28th, 15 inches lay at Pontefract; on 28th-29th, 15 inches at Woodthorpe, Notts.; on 29th, two feet at Malvern, 23 inches at Sheffield, and 20 inches at Bolton with drifts of ten to twelve feet. Birmingham had 15 inches lying on 29th and 30th.

May 9, 1943.—Six inches of snow fell at Douglas, Isle of Man. This would be a most exceptional fall for this place even in mid-winter.

February 27, 1944.—A great snowstorm gave a depth of 16 inches of snow at Nottingham in about 12 hours.

March 1, 1944.—Snow drifts 30 feet deep at Lairg, Sutherland.

January 25, 1945.—A great snowstorm at Cardiff gave an undrifted depth of 30 inches.

H

In 1947 most of Great Britain had continuous snow cover from January 27th to March 13th, a period of 46 days. At Woodthorpe, Notts., snow lay continuously for 56 days.

Many of these storms refer to the southern half of England, and the storms of January, 1881, and March, 1891, are regarded as historical. It is well, therefore, to realise that storms of a fury unknown in the south are relatively common on the desolate highlands of the Pennine Chain, the Grampian Mountains and the Cairngorms. To be far from shelter in such blizzards means almost certain death. It is because these areas are so sparsely populated that little is heard of these savage visitations.

CHAPTER XVI.

Sunshine and Shade

Britain's countryside, whether lowland or hill, cliff or cornfield, looks most beautiful when flooded with sunshine. It is a tradition with us that we do not see enough of the sun. Rarely do we get such a sequence of cloudless sunny days that they become monotonous. Nor, let us be thankful, do we endure weeks and months of sun blazing down on bare, burnt-up fields. Unbroken sunshine induces lethargy. Most of the time our sky is happily varied by broken cloud sending travelling shadows over town and country. In summer a grey day may have the effect of a restful smile of a quiet woman, coming after the tiring erotic charms of a glamour girl.

Clouds vary in appearance, density and height. Highest of all are the wispy curls of the cirrus cloud. They often foretell unsettled weather. Lower than the cirrus are the towering cumulus clouds, which may develop into a thunderstorm. An exile from the northern fells living in London once said, "We look at the cumulus and try to imagine they are our "mountains." In winter a low grey cloud called strato-cumulus may pass in unbroken sheets for wearying hours.

A scale of 0 to 10 is used in estimating the amount of cloud in the sky, 0 being cloudless and 10 overcast. On this scale the average amount of cloud in Britain is from 6 to 7.5. At Portsmouth, for the year as a whole, it is 5.9, at Falmouth 6.0, York 6.3, Manchester 7.4 and Glasgow 7.8. At Kew cloud is least in September and May, with means of 5.8 and 6.1. It reaches a maximum in December and January, when it is 7.4. At Falmouth it varies from 5.2 in April and May to 6.8 in December. At Stornaway and in the Shetlands it is considerable at all seasons.

Sunshine is not recorded by a dignified old gentleman with a white beard and a stop-watch, as one lady supposed, but by a standardised spherical lens which focuses the sun's rays on a specially prepared graduated card on which a trace is burned. This instrument has to be placed so that it receives the sun uninterruptedly from sunrise to sunset.

For the year as a whole the sun is above the horizon for twelve hours a day in all districts of the British Isles, but varies considerably from winter to summer. In the South of England the sun is up for 8 hours a day in December and 16¼ hours in June, but in the Shetlands it is about 6 hours in December and 18½ hours in June.

In the sunniest parts of the south the sun will shine about half the possible time in the summer. In the Midlands and North amounts are generally below 40 per cent. of the possible. On the West Coast of Scotland the percentage of sunshine is highest in April and May, and the Isle of Man shows the same peculiarity, though June in the island has as high a percentage as April.

In winter the proportion is much less, being 20 per cent. or less. The Channel Isles are Britain's sunniest spots. At Guernsey the yearly average is 1885 hours, or five hours ten minutes a day, and Jersey enjoys 1864 hours. Official records show Worthing and Eastbourne at the head of the sunshine tables on the mainland, with 1,834 and 1,833 hours respectively. "You ought to go to New Zealand for sunshine," said someone, "they get eight hours a day for the year." I should like to know where in New Zealand the average is eight hours a day. Wellington averages 2,000 hours a year, or nearly 5½ hours per day, which is slightly more than our sunniest places. Examples of extremely sunny climates are Kimberley, 3,430 hours, and Johannesburg, 3,200 hours in South Africa, and Alexandria, Egypt, with 3,430 hours. These places have an average of nine hours a day or rather more.

Figures 31, 32 and 33 show the distribution of average sunshine in summer, winter and for the year. The East Coast south of the Wash, all the South Coast and Pembrokeshire have over seven hours a day in June and the extreme North of Scotland less than 5½ hours. In December the sunniest places have over 1½ hours a day.

In general, coastal areas are sunnier than inland districts. In and near large towns sunshine is reduced by smoke, particularly in winter. This is well exemplified by London. At Bunhill Row, in the City, the December average is only 11 hours, and at Westminster 22 hours, compared with 35 hours at Hampstead, 36 hours at Enfield, 37 hours at Kew and 38 hours at Croydon. Fog also reduces the amount of sunshine in winter, especially in and near large towns. As fog occurs very often with a high barometer places in a foggy zone may record no sun on a particular day, while others not far away may have several hours.

Oldham Road, Manchester, has the smallest annual average of sunshine in Britain, 967 hours. Whitworth Park, Manchester, averages 1,029, and Fort Augustus 996 hours. Other places with low sunshine values are Bolton 1,032 hours, Lerwick 1,089 hours, Burnley 1,112 hours, Huddersfield 1,147 hours, Wakefield 1,162 hours and Bradford 1,215. No doubt other industrial towns in

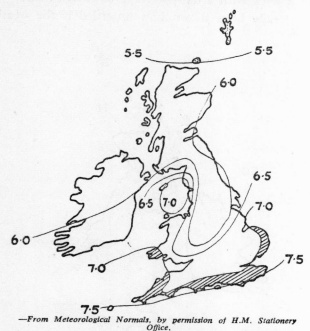

—From Meteorological Normals, by permission of H.M. Stationery Office.

FIG 31. AVERAGE SUNSHINE IN JUNE (HOURS PER DAY).

East Lancashire and West Yorkshire have poor records, but no information is available.

In a very sunny year more than 2,000 hours of sunshine may be recorded at favoured places in Britain. The year 1933 was remarkably fine and among the highest totals were Hastings 2,020 hours, Worthing 2,100 hours, Jersey 2,176 hours, and Guernsey 2,135 hours. Ventnor reported 2,150 hours. These latter values mean a daily average of almost six hours. In the very sunny year of 1893 Jersey aggregated as much as 2,340 hours or six hours twenty-five minutes a day.

Occasionally in an exceptional month the daily average will reach ten or even twelve hours a day, which can vie with records in the sunniest parts of the world. Such a month was the very dry June of 1925 (whose rainfall was mentioned in an earlier chapter). In that month Falmouth recorded 382 hours, or nearly 12¾ hours per day. The astonishing nature of this brilliant month is better imagined when we consider how unusual it is to have even a week with a daily average of twelve hours.

It has already been shown how unsettled is the weather in

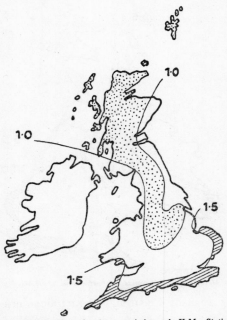

—*From Meteorological Normals, by permission of H.M. Stationery Office.*
FIG. 32.   AVERAGE SUNSHINE IN DECEMBER (HOURS PER DAY).

the Shetlands with very frequent, though not really heavy, rain. In June in these far northern islands the sun is above the horizon for over 18½ hours a day, but owing to cloudy skies the average June sunshine is about 5½ hours a day. It will be obvious that should settled cloudless weather prevail for a time in these latitudes very large daily amounts of sunshine would be recorded. In June, 1930, for a period of eight days (10th to 17th) the Shet-

lands had a most brilliant spell with a daily average of almost
15 hours. On June 14, 1930, Stornoway had 18 hours of sunshine, which is virtually the maximum possible in one day in
the British Isles.

June 23 and 24, 1934, were two brilliant days at Lerwick with
17.3 and 17.4 hours of sun respectively.

It has been remarked that the North-West of Britain is subject to large amounts of sunshine in spring and early summer.

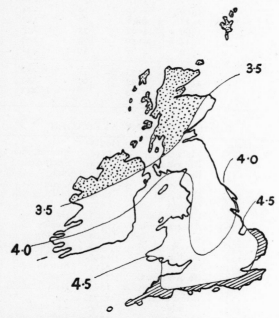

—*From Meteorological Normals, by permission of H.M. Stationery Office.*
FIG. 33. AVERAGE SUNSHINE FOR THE YEAR (HOURS PER DAY).

In April, 1935, Douglas, Isle of Man, was the sunniest place in our
islands with a total of 202 hours. In the following May the
three largest totals for the whole country were 299 hours at the
Point of Ayre, Isle of Man, 305 hours at Tiree, off the West
Coast of Argyll, and 307 hours at Turnberry in Ayrshire. But
some people will still go on saying that we do not get much sunshine.

TABLE IX.—DULL DAYS AND SUNNY DAYS

		Annual Average Sunshine, hours	Hours per day	Sunless days	Days up to nine hours	Days with nine hours
Deerness	.. ..	1127	3.08	91	245	29
Aberdeen	.. ..	1329	3.64	74	258	33
Renfrew	.. ..	1193	3.27	91	247	27
Douglas, I.O.M.	..	1574	4.31	75	234	56
Morpeth	.. ..	1381	3.78	78	250	37
Southport	.. ..	1510	4.13	70	244	51
Cambridge	.. ..	1525	4.18	76	241	48
Kew	.. ..	1469	4.02	73	248	44
Southampton	..	1644	4.50	63	244	58
Falmouth	.. ..	1710	4.68	59	242	64
Armagh	.. ..	1289	3.53	79	252	34
Dublin	.. ..	1437	3.93	67	257	41
Valentia	.. ..	1368	3.75	76	245	44

SOME SUNSHINE AVERAGES

	Hours		Hours		Hours
Guernsey ..	1885	Malvern ..	1548	Birmingham ..	1304
Jersey ..	1864	Ilfracombe ..	1542	Sheffield ..	1276
Eastbourne ..	1833	Bath	1540	Nairn	1274
Sandown,		Llandudno ..	1528	Oban	1274
I.O.W.	1814	Blackpool ..	1505	Nottingham ..	1265
Ventnor, I.O.W.	1792	Oxford ..	1501	York	1249
Margate ..	1780	Cheltenham ..	1485	Ilkley	1223
Felixstowe ..	1769	Aberystwyth ..	1485	Paisley ..	1218
Torquay ..	1767	Kew	1469	Buxton ..	1216
Brighton ..	1761	Liverpool ..	1448	Bradford ..	1215
Bournemouth ..	1758	Bridlington ..	1447	Keswick ..	1215
Falmouth ..	1710	Whitby ..	1413	Stornoway ..	1215
Scilly Isles ..	1708	St. Andrews ..	1412	Stirling ..	1209
Newquay ..	1677	Scarborough ..	1393	Huddersfield ..	1147
Plymouth ..	1677	Edinburgh ..	1373	Burnley ..	1112
Southend ..	1654	Dundee ..	1366	Lerwick ..	1089
Yarmouth ..	1643	Harrogate ..	1359	Bolton	1032
Tenby	1636	Perth	1357	Manchester	
Tunbridge		Leamington ..	1347	(Whit. Park)	1029
Wells	1630	Hull	1327	Fort Augustus	996
Skegness ..	1597	Dumfries ..	1316	Manchester	
Cromer ..	1585	Durham ..	1315	(Oldham Road)	967

CHAPTER XVII.

WHY WE GO TO THE COAST

THE British are said to be a nation of seafarers. An unbiased observer might doubt this if he examined a ship-load of passengers going to the Isle of Man or the Channel Islands in a choppy sea. But the call of the sea causes millions of people to gravitate to our coasts in summer. And what a magnificent coast it is! The urge must be great which impels so many to accept the discomforts of over-crowded boarding houses and hotels in the height of the holiday season. What causes this urge? It may not be the sea itself; comparatively few are so developed aesthetically as to be able to adopt a Yogi-like contemplation of the waves for a fortnight or more.

Perhaps it is the "sea air." "You can smell the ozone at Corcombe, old man!" This is not true. The amount of ozone is so small that one could not possibly smell it. What one does smell is the fresh salt tang of air blowing from the sea which has a particularly tonic effect on dwellers in inland towns, whose air is apt to feel heavy and stale in warm weather. We accept the sea as our birthright but millions of people in Europe have rarely or never seen it.

The main features of a coastal climate as compared with an inland one are. lower day and higher night temperatures on the coast, more sunshine, and the invigorating effect of the sea air.

On an average, a July day is 4° F. cooler at Brighton than in London, and Skegness is 4° F. or 5° F. cooler than Lincoln. The effects of the sea are very local on some days. If a light breeze is blowing from the sea on a day of hot sunshine the temperature less than a mile inland is appreciably higher than on the beach. Weymouth, on a summer afternoon, will average 4½° F. warmer than Portland Bill jutting into the sea. In July and August day temperatures are 2° F. lower at Yarmouth than at Norwich, and the highest on record at Yarmouth is 89° F. compared with 96° F. at Norwich.

Skegness, on the Lincolnshire coast, faces east, but Hunstanton, just across the Wash, faces west. A July day at Hunstanton averages 1½° F. higher than at Skegness, and the warmest day of the summer will be 80° F. at Skegness and 85° F. at Hunstanton, the latter being as high as inland places like Lincoln and Nottingham. September 19, 1926, was an exceptionally warm day over England (page 87). On that day, with an air current from east to south, the thermometer at Hunstanton reached 89° F., forming a remarkable contrast with the maximum of 77° F. at Skegness.

Figure 34 shows what happens during a sea breeze on a warm summer day. The wind comes in cool from the sea, rising in temperature as it passes inland over the sun-warmed earth. At some distance inland it meets the prevailing wind circulation, rises upwards and turns back seawards at some height above the ground. Over the coast there will be a temperature inversion. Mr. E. G.

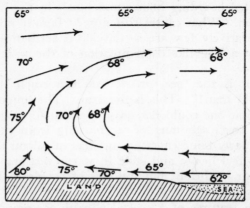

FIG. 34.   TEMPERATURE IN A SEA BREEZE.

Bilham, in his book, "The Climate of the British Isles," points out that this may produce more stable air conditions on the coast than inland and so lessen the risk of thunderstorms.

On the coast a summer morning may be warm, the sea breeze setting in about midday and giving a cooler afternoon, which in its turn may give place to warmer air in the early evening when the sea breeze dies away. The sea breeze develops more strongly on the East Coast than elsewhere because in spring and summer the difference between the sea and air temperatures over the land is greater than on other coasts. At most coastal places the thermometers are only visited once a day to obtain the maximum and minimum readings, and not many thermographs are in use. Consequently, observations of temperature changes during the sea breeze are not numerous.

On May 21, 1922, the thermometer at Skegness was 76° F. at 2 p.m. G.M.T., with a light southerly wind. Shortly after 2 p.m. gusts of cool air came in from the east and north-east, the thermometer falling to 67° F. by 3 p.m. On May 23, 1922, a wind from the sea prevailed till 1 p.m., when the thermometer showed 69° F. The wind then shifted to south-west and at 1.30 p.m. the thermometer stood at 80° F., a rise of 11° F. in half an hour. At 3.30 p.m. the thermometer registered the high May level of 82° F., when a sea breeze set in, lowering the temperature to 69° F. by 4 p.m., a fall of 13° F. in half an hour in sunny weather. The physical sensation was a change from great heat to pleasant coolness in this short space of time.

Eire is like a rampart protecting England in some degree from the influence of the Atlantic. It may be deduced that if Eire did not exist England would have slightly cooler summers and slightly milder winters, with probably some increase in rainfall. If the North Sea were dry land our winters would be cooler and summers warmer.

Coastal climates have much less fog than inland areas, particularly in autumn and winter. Summer fogs, or sea mists, occur on the coast. There is more breeze than inland, with a greater tendency for gales. There is less frost than inland. On the East Coast the winds from north-east and east can be very bitter and searching right up to the end of May. Autumn on the East Coast is generally mild and pleasant, really cold winds not being much in evidence before Christmas.

In spring and summer it is not uncommon for day temperatures on the Lincolnshire coast to be 10° F. or 15° F. lower than inland. Occasionally the difference is as much as 20° F., or a similar difference as between a day in January and early June. A few examples are given to illustrate this.

				Skegness	Nottingham
June 30, 1934	...	...	...	63° F.	83° F.
July 6, 1934	...	...	...	66°	87°
July 8, 1934	...	...	...	67°	87°
July 9, 1934	...	...	...	65°	86°
July 10, 1934	...	...	...	68°	88°
July 11, 1934	...	...	...	70°	90°
July 6, 1939	...	...	...	64°	84°

All these cases occurred with a wind from the sea. Two other examples are given to show how intense is the effect of a change in wind direction on the East Coast in spring.

			Skegness	Nottingham	
May 11, 1934	...	...	57° F.	78° F.	Wind from Sea
May 12, 1934	...	...	77°	79°	South-west wind from the land.
April 11, 1939	...	...	51°	71°	Wind from sea
April 12, 1939	...	...	73°	74°	South-west wind from the land

It will be seen that the shift of wind from sea to land raised the temperature by 20° F. in the first case, and 22° F. in the second, but had little effect on the thermometer at Nottingham.

CHAPTER XVIII.

Is It Bracing or Relaxing?

WHAT constitutes a bracing climate? And why are some places relaxing? Such places as Scarborough, Skegness, Cromer, Yarmouth, Brighton, Eastbourne and Newquay are said to be bracing. Others, such as Bournemouth, Ventnor, Torquay, Falmouth and Penzance are regarded as relaxing. Yet Falmouth and Newquay are only a few miles apart.

Can we tabulate the factors which make a place bracing or otherwise? What effect have temperature, wind, sunshine and humidity?

A cool temperature is more bracing than heat. The air is more tonic when a breeze is blowing than when it is calm or nearly so. Sea air is more bracing than land air. It is generally agreed that dry air is more bracing than damp air. Contrast the pleasing freshness of a dry west wind with the sultry feeling of a humid southerly wind in thundery weather.

Sunshine is a tonic, but in hot weather it can cause languor and weariness.

These facts are fairly obvious. If they are accepted then a bracing locality is one with a dry air, plenty of breeze, and sunshine with a cool air.

Our bracing seaside resorts would fulfil this definition in a greater or less degree. When we examine things in greater detail some snags appear. The humidity of the air on the coast at bracing resorts in summer is higher than at relaxing places inland, which seems contradictory. On the bracing Sussex coast the humidity will be 70 per cent., as against 60 per cent. in languid London. The average afternoon humidity at bracing Yarmouth in July is 74 per cent., compared with 65 per cent. at Nottingham and Birmingham. Bracing Blackpool will have a higher humidity very often than relaxing Manchester. Mr. G. Manley cites the case of Durham as a rather relaxing yet comparatively cold climate. Mere coolness is not necessarily bracing. Beyond a certain limit it becomes raw and depressing.

We know that inland in summer the air feels fresher and less tiring when humidity is low, yet if we go to the sea we find the air tonic with a higher humidity. In spite of this it would not do to regard humidity as unimportant.

Another factor is height above sea level. A place at a considerable elevation is cooler and has more wind than one on the plains, and therefore is more bracing. Buxton, at 1,000 feet, has a tonic bracing climate. A summer day there averages 4° F. cooler than Manchester. Hindhead, in Surrey, at 900 feet is bracing Other bracing places are Harrogate (480 feet), Malvern (500 feet) and Matlock Bank (600 feet). Matlock Bath (300 feet) in the valley of the River Derwent and about two miles from Matlock Bank, tends to be relaxing. In Wales, Llandrindod Wells (750 feet) is bracing, and Scotland has such places as Braemar (1,100 feet), Ballater (660 feet) and Peebles (500 feet). Relative height is also important. Woodhall Spa, Lincolnshire, is situated only 40 feet above sea level, but it stands on a platform above the fens and open to all winds. It may be classed as relatively tonic.

Plains and river valleys are more relaxing than the surrounding country. Anyone living a few miles out of a town who goes into it in the early morning in summer will notice the difference in the atmosphere. The country air feels fresh and cool; that of the town seems stuffy. The sun beating down on city buildings warms them, so that at night the mass of masonry acts as a radiator, preventing summer nights from cooling off as quickly as in the country. When the country is varied, relatively bracing and relaxing climates may be found near together. The climate of Hampstead (450 feet) is bracing relative to that of London as a whole. At Nottingham that part of the city adjoining the Trent at an elevation of 80 feet is relaxing compared with the breezy height of Mapperley at 400 feet.

One becomes accustomed to the locality where one lives, so that "bracing" and "relaxing" become relative terms. To a Southampton man, Nottingham seems bracing, but to a Skegness or Yarmouth man it feels relaxing.

Places on the sea coast sheltered from the sea winds are often relaxing. Some people prefer bracing climates, and those jaded with work in stuffy towns find at the seaside a more effective tonic than ever came out of a doctor's medicine bottle. They can take it all day, instead of three times a day after meals. On the other hand, some people, such as certain types of invalids and elderly people, like a relaxing climate. Such people sometimes say that the air of the East Coast is too "strong" for them.

Professor K. C. Edwards, M.A., Ph.D., of Nottingham University, raised the question whether those who worked in towns really benefited by a holiday in a bracing resort. He suggested that such a climate tended to make them over-exert themselves when they needed rest, and that possibly a relaxing climate, inducing less desire for strenuous exercise might be of greater benefit. It is certainly an interesting point for discussion.

Eventually, we shall have more knowledge of the effect of local climates on the human body and on health than is the case now.

CHAPTER XIX.

Is Your Favourite Climate Here?—I

HAVING considered the British Isles in a general way, the east with its large temperature ranges and low rainfall, the softer rainier climate of the west, the heavy rains of the mountains, and the breezes of the coast, let us get a picture of the peculiarities of some individual districts.

Devon and Cornwall.

The south-west peninsula of England has a great reputation for its mildness. As the surface is varied and the sea washes it on north and south, considerable differences of temperature and rainfall occur. Devon may be divided into three, the low-lying inland districts, the high land and the coast. The climate of the low-lying parts is relaxing. Summer heat approaches that of the Midlands. The high land is cooler and less enervating, but subject to considerable rain and low cloud. The coast is mild and often relaxing with less rain than on high ground. The humidity makes it rather enervating at times in the summer.

None of the coastal resorts experience the very high temperatures which occur at times in summer over eastern England. At Torquay an average July afternoon is 68½° F., compared with 71½° F. at Cullompton. The highest temperature on record at Torquay and Plymouth is 87° F. in July, 1923. In January, 1940, Plymouth and Torquay fell to 16° F. An average warmest day of the summer is 80° F. at Torquay and Ilfracombe, 79° F. at Plymouth. The coldest night of the winter may be expected to fall to 28° F. at Ilfracombe, 27° F. at Torquay, and 25° F. at Plymouth. Inland temperatures are more extreme on low ground. In July, 1923, Killerton reached 94° F. and Cullompton 92° F. In the severe January of 1940, Cullompton registered the very low temperature of 2° F. On an average, Cullompton varies from 85° F. to 20° F. (similar to the Midlands) in the course of a year.

On Dartmoor a very different climate exists. Princetown, at 1,400 feet, has a record for bleakness and damp. Rainfall is heavy, amounting to 82 inches per annum, compared with 37 inches at Plymouth, 35 inches at Newton Abbot, 33 inches at Torquay, and 31 inches at Exeter. Fog is very frequent on Dartmoor, and may be expected to a greater or less degree on 100 days a year, but this fog is low cloud, not fog of the radiation type. Princetown in summer averages 5° F. cooler than Torquay. In August, 1932, Princetown reached a maximum temperature of 86° F. compared with 78° F. at Torquay, an excellent example of how the effect of the sea can sometimes more than counterbalance the result of 1,400 feet of altitude.

Cornwall is similar to lowland Devon, but more insular. It is less subject to extremes of warmth and cold. There is no area of very high rainfall similar to Dartmoor, but lowland Cornwall has rather more rain that lowland Devon.

The Isle of Wight.

The Isle of Wight has a sunny rather relaxing climate. It is separated from the mainland by a narrow strip of water about four miles wide. It has not, therefore, a very insular climate but more resembles that of the adjoining mainland. Over a period of 18 years the average hottest day of the year was 81° F. at Ventnor, 82° F. at Ryde, but 86½° F. at Newport, near the centre of the island. The average daily variation in temperature for the year was 10° F. at Ventnor, 11° F at Ryde and Sandown, but as much as 15° F. at Newport. The coldest night of the year varied from 26° F. at Ventnor, 25° F. at Ryde, and 24° F. at Sandown to 20° F. at Newport. Newport's temperature ranges are similar to those of inland England. The island is one of the sunniest areas in Britan.

The Scilly Isles.

This little group of islands off the toe of Cornwall is typical of a highly-developed insular climate. All Britain is insular compared with Central Europe and Russia, but England appears "continental" in contrast to Scilly. It has already been shown that temperature can vary more in less than twelve hours in England than in a year at Scilly, where sometimes the range is only 10° F. in a month. In the exceptionally mild December of 1934 every day at Scilly reached 50° F., and so constant was the temperature that the warmest day was only 4° F. above the coolest.

Summer heat is little felt in Scilly, days as high as 70° F. being few.

I

The Scillies have a good record of sunshine, and the annual rainfall of 32 inches is 10 inches less than at Penzance. Snow is rare, and thunder much less frequent than in most parts of England.

The Channel Islands.

This group of islands possesses the sunniest and mildest climate in the British Isles. The islands are famous for their flowers, fruit and vegetables, upon which the whole economy of the group is based. The mean annual temperature of Guernsey is similar to that of Scilley, and Jersey is a fraction of a degree milder. Winter in the Channel Islands is not quite so mild as at Penzance and the Scillies, but summer is rather warmer. The climate is equable, but Jersey is subject to larger temperature ranges than the other islands, partly owing to its larger size and partly to its proximity to the mainland of France. The mean temperature of Jersey varies from 43.1° F. in February to 63.5° F. in August, and Guernsey from 43.3° F. to 61.7° F. Average daily temperature range is 10° F. in Jersey and 8° F. in Guernsey. A summer afternoon in Jersey will be 3° F. warmer than in Guernsey on an average, and a Jersey winter night 2° F. colder than Guernsey.

The rather general impression that the Channel Islands are intensely hot in summer (quite tropical, my dear!) is erroneous, and due to the north-south fallacy. A summer afternoon in Jersey averages the same as in York, and several degrees cooler than London.

Both the highest summer and lowest winter temperatures occur when the wind is blowing from the Continent. Very high temperatures do not develop in small islands, but are "imported" from the nearest mainland. Records kept at Jersey from 1871 to 1931 showed an upper limit of 90° F. on July 23, 1873, and again on July 6, 1923, but on August 19, 1932 (when temperature was exceptionally high over England and France—page 87) the thermometer in Jersey rose to the phenomenal height of 96° F., and in Guernsey to 88° F. On an average the hottest day of the year is 83° F. at Jersey and 79° F. at Guernsey.

On January 18, 1891, with an east wind from the Continent the thermometer at Jersey fell to 12° F., which is 13° F. lower than anything ever recorded in the Scillies. On an average the coldest night of the year is 25° F. at Jersey and 29° F. at Guernsey. Snow does not often fall. Fog is mainly of the sea-mist type, and can be very dangerous to shipping round these rocky coasts. Rainfall averages 33 inches at Jersey and 36 inches in Guernsey. Guernsey is more bracing than the larger island.

A Valley near Rickmansworth.

In 1929 Mr. E. L. Hawke, M.A., F.R.A.S., Secretary of the Royal Meteorological Society, established a weather station in a valley bottom of the foothills of the Chilterns, midway between Rickmansworth and Chorleywood, in Hertfordshire. It soon became apparent that here was the most "continental" climate yet discovered in the British Isles. Over a period of 13 years (1930 to 1942) observations were taken which give a picture of its unusual conditions. For the 13 years the mean annual maximum temperature was 58.1° F., and the mean annual minimum 36.4° F., giving an average daily range of 21.7° F. No other place in Britain where records have been kept has so large a range, few places reaching 16° F. In June the average daily variation is 27° F. One may expect a maximum of 90° F. on the hottest day of the year and 10° F. on the coldest night. A temperature of 95.5° F. occurred on July 31, 1943, and the other extreme was −0.3° F. on January 20, 1940. On the grass a reading of −7.5° F. occurred in January, 1942. Frost has been recorded every month of the year. Mr. E. G. Bilham has pointed out that the night temperature here is almost exactly similar to that of the Aberdeen-shire plateau (see page 127), which is about the coldest inhabited region of the British Isles. It is rather disconcerting to find that a little valley a mere twenty miles from London has such extreme night temperatures.

Just before midnight on April 18, 1936, the temperature in the screen on this valley bottom was 25° F., but only 40 feet higher up the hillside it was 36½° F., an astonishing difference in so short a space. A range of 51° F. has occurred here between early morning and afternoon, and a range of 50° F. was recorded on September 4, 1940 (90.1° F. to 39.7° F.) and on July 7, 1941 (92.1° F. to 42.0° F.). The temperature in the sun has been known to reach 150° F. only a few hours after a grass minimum of 26° F. On July 7, 1930, a maximum temperature of 175° F. was registered in the sun's rays. The mean night temperature is at or below freezing point in the screen for about two-fifths of the year, and on the grass for three-fifths of the year. On an average there are 134 night frosts in the screen in twelve months (about twice that general in the English Midlands) and 203 nights with ground frost. This climate is the antithesis of the equable Scilly Isles. Plant life has a very strenuous and unhappy time.

The Fens.

This low-lying tract of flat land stretches from Cambridge and Bedfordshire northwards into Lincolnshire. It may be said to extend to the warp lands at the head of the Humber. Much of the fens is very little above sea level, and rivers are artificially dyked. The climate is relaxing. Summers are warm, and winters cold. A temperature of 96° F. has been attained as far north as Lincoln. At the other extreme a reading as low as −8° F. was reported from Stamford in February, 1895.

Annual rainfall in the fens is less than 25 inches a year. Wisbech 23 inches, March 23 inches and Cambridge 22 inches, are typical of the region.

Buxton.

In Britain population at or above 1,000 feet above sea level is sparse. Buxton is unique in being the only town of any size which reaches this altitude. There are a few villages higher up in the world, such as Nenthead on the Northern Pennines at 1,300 to 1,500 feet.

The climate of Buxton is tonic and bracing. It lies in a high valley with surrounding hills rising to the 1,200 to 1,600 feet level. In this hilly district rainfall is rather large, amounting at Buxton to 48 inches per annum. April is the driest month with 2.94 inches, and December, 5.67 inches, is the wettest. Over a period of a quarter of a century the average number of rain days is 212 in a year. A January day at Buxton is 3½° F. colder than at Nottingham, and a July day 5° F. cooler.

The highest temperature on record at Buxton is 89° F. recorded on July 16, 1876, and the lowest −11° F. on February 11, 1895. This latter appears to be the lowest official temperature reading ever made in England. Spring comes late in Buxton. With the low winter mean temperature coupled with considerable rainfall, snow may fall to a great depth when conditions are favourable.

The North Wales Coast.

The strip of the coast from the River Dee to the neighbourhood of Llandudno is well-known to holiday-makers. Its remarkably favourable winter climate is not so famous as it deserves to be. This coast lies in the shelter of the Snowdon mountain mass, and has a low rainfall with very mild winters.   It is a northern riviera.

The mean temperature of January at Llandudno and Colwyn Bay is 42½° F., and Rhyl 1° F. less.   More than half of the South Coast is colder than this in winter, Brighton and Bournemouth being 41° F., Torquay 43° F. and Falmouth 44° F.   It is, therefore, unnecessary for northerners to go south for winter warmth; it is waiting for them on their own doorstep.   In summer the South Coast of England is rather warmer than North Wales.   At Llandudno the average warmest day of the summer is 81° F., and the coldest night 25° F., compared with 80° F. and 27° F. at Torquay.

An interesting feature of this coast is that the south-west wind passing over Snowdonia is robbed of its moisture and this dry air is warmed by compression as it passes down the northern slopes of the mountains.   As a result the winter afternoon temperature can sometimes rival anything ever recorded elsewhere in Britain in January.   A reading as high as 63° F. has been recorded in January at Rhyl and Colwyn Bay, and 62° F. at Llandudno, whereas Falmouth has not risen above 56° F. and Jersey 57° F. in January.   Here is an excellent example of a district in Britain being warmer than many places further south.

No less favourable a factor for the North Wales coast is the low rainfall.   Rhyl averages 26 inches per annum, Llandudno 30 inches, and Colwyn Bay 31 inches, considerably less than the warmest resorts in the south.   Indeed, the North Wales coast has less rain than any resort in the south with as mild a winter. Sunshine along this favoured coast averages 1,500 to 1,600 hours a year, and there is a marked absence of fog and frost.

The Isle of Man.

This island, about 33 miles long and a dozen miles across, has an insular climate compared with the mainland, but not so insular as the Scilly Isles.   Its climate is pleasant, healthy and tonic.   The summers are not so hot as in the English lowlands, and the winters are similar in mean temperature to those of Jersey or the Devon coast.   Sunshine is considerable, about 1,600 hours a year, and greater than in any other part of the British Isles as far north.   Rainfall is not excessive, considering the mountainous nature of the island, and is much less than that of

134 THIS WEATHER OF OURS

the Lake District, Snowdonia or Dartmoor. Douglas has an annual rainfall of 42 inches and Ramsey an inch or so more. The wettest period of the year is from October to December, of which December has 5 inches. The driest season is from April to June, each of which months averages 2½ inches. Rain days average 205, which is not frequent for the West Coast.

Snow falls on 15 days a year, but lies on the ground on only four days. Frost occurs on only 17 nights in a year (and is rarely severe), compared with 46 nights at Kew and 13 at Falmouth.

Most of our knowledge of the island comes from the Douglas records. The highest temperature on record at Douglas is 82° F. on July 30, 1948. The lowest is 11° F. on February 9, 1895, which is only 1° F. lower than the minimum for Jersey. On an average the year's warmest day is 76° F., and coldest night 26° F. Only on five occasions since 1878 has 80° F. been reached at Douglas. An ordinary August day is 63° F. and a February one 45° F. It is probable that temperatures slightly in excess of 82° F. have been attained in the valleys of the Dhoo, Greeba and Neb. One wonders if Port Erin is the "Penzance" of the island. No records are available.

Radiation fogs are rare, but sea mists occur at times. The mountain road from Douglas to Ramsey reaches a height of 1,400 feet near Snaefell Mountain, and one hears of "fog" on this road. This is really low cloud, which not uncommonly covers the mountains down to 1,000 feet in unsettled weather.

Heavy rain in the island is usually of the depression type, and not of the thunder type as in England.

Strong winds occur in autumn and winter, and gales are severe at times. Owing to the mild winters exotic plants such as the veronica, escallonia and fuchsias thrive outdoors in almost any situation, and geraniums grow up walls. Palm trees reach heights of ten feet or more.

CHAPTER XX.

Is Your Favourite Climate Here? II.

The Hebrides.

THE islands off the West Coast of Scotland have a very insular climate. Summers are cool, winters mild. Frost and snow are uncommon. Rainfall is very frequent, but amounts are not nearly so large as in mountainous districts on the mainland. Winds can be very strong, but in sheltered places myrtles, fuchsias and palms flourish outdoors all the year.

The highest temperature recorded at Stornoway is 78° F. in June, 1911, and the lowest 11° F. in January, 1918. An average summer's warmest day is 72° F., and winter's coldest night 21° F. A July afternoon averages 61° F., similar to May in the southern half of England. In January Stornoway is no colder than Brighton or Eastbourne. Spring (April to June) is the sunniest, driest season in the Hebrides. The smaller islands have even milder winters.

The island of Tiree, 14 miles long and five miles wide, has an average daily temperature variation of 7.7° F., as in Scilly, but it is 4° F. cooler than Scilly. The average hottest day of the year is 71° F. and the coldest night 27° F., compared with 85° F. and 19° F. at Kew. Barra Island is even more insular and equable than Tiree, for the average daily range is only 5.2° F. So dominant is the effect of the sea winds here than the strong summer sun raises the day temperature little above the night. The average warmest day of the year is 67° F. and the coldest night 31° F., giving a yearly range of only 36° F., compared with 40° F. at Scilly and 65° F. in central England. It is interesting to notice that on Barra February and March are the coldest months of the year, and April is only 1° F. higher than January. A July day is only 13° F. warmer than a February day. Winter in Barra is similar in temperature to Jersey, though less liable to frost than the southern island, and rather warmer than Ventnor.

The Shetland Islands

The Shetland Islands appeal to the imagination because they are Britain's furthest north. It is not generally realised that they are further north than Oslo or Stockholm. Lerwick is about the same distance from Aberdeen as it is from Bergen in Norway. The Shetlands are a group of islands, mostly very small, numbering about one hundred, of which about thirty are inhabited.

"The frost and snow must be terrible," someone once remarked to me, and it was a very natural comment. It is not true to fact. The sea gives the Shetlands as equable a climate as the Scilly Isles, but rather cooler, the mean annual temperature at Lerwick being 48.5° F., compared with 50.2° F. at Kew and 52.2° F. in the Scillies. Winter in the Shetlands is warmer than in inland England, but summer is cooler than anywhere else in Britain, except at high elevations.

Rainfall amounts to 40 inches per annum, and is very frequent, falling on an average on 260 days at Lerwick and almost 300 days in places. On many days amounts are trivial, but the frequency of rain exemplifies the unsettled nature of the weather in the islands. Temperature is at its minimum in February and March is as cold or colder than January. Daylight in winter is very short. The winters, therefore, though not severe, are long and depressing. The coldest night of winter averages 22° F., compared with 19° F. at Kew and 17° F. at Oxford. At Lerwick the lowest temperature on record is 16° F. on January 14, 1918, which forms an ironical contrast with Jersey's low record of 12° F.

Snow is frequent, falling on 39 days a year, but it usually thaws as it falls, for it lies on only eight days, which is less than in inland England. A July or August day would seem very chilly to an Englishman, the afternoon temperature averaging 57° F. or 58° F., a level in keeping with the end of April in England. The warmest day of the summer averages 65° F., compared with 85° F. in the English midlands. Lerwick's high record is 73° F. on June 6, 1939, but 77° F. was recorded at Baltasound, in the extreme north, on July 12, 1926.

The Upper Dee Valley, Aberdeenshire

The valley of the Upper Dee, west of Aboyne, has a distinctive climate. Here are Ballater, Balmoral and Braemar. The valley is flanked by the Cairngorms and Grampians. Its climate is bracing, and considering the mountainous nature of the surrounding country the rainfall is low, being 35 inches at Braemar and 33 inches at Balmoral. The mean annual temperature is low, being 43.3° F. at Braemar, or 3° F. less than at Aberdeen. As one might expect in a high valley, the nights are notably cold. Mean minimum temperature is below freezing point from November to March, reaching its lowest 29.0° in February, and being only 32.7° in April. Braemar holds the official record for low temperature, −17° F., in the British Isles. Temperatures below zero have been recorded in November, December, January, February and March. Night frost has occurred some time in every month of the year, the lowest in July being 30° F. and August 29° F. When conditions are favourable high temperatures can take place in summer. A reading of 88° F. has been registered at Balmoral, which is nearly as high as anything known in Scotland, and only 4° F. below the highest on record at York. Snow falls on about 50 days a year and lies on the ground on 60 days. The air is notably free from smoke and dust. A July afternoon at Braemar averages 63.9° F., or 1.7° F. warmer than at Aberdeen. Balmoral has an average annual temperature range from 78° F. to 8° F.

Ben Nevis

Ben Nevis, Britain's highest mountain, set meteorologists wondering what sort of a climate existed up there, 4,406 feet above sea level. Regular observations were kept on the summit from 1884 to 1903, and valuable information was obtained about this bleak spot. The mean annual temperature is 31.5° F., so that we may describe the conditions as Arctic, for this value equals that for Jan Mayen. Mean temperature is below freezing from October to April and only 1° F. above in May. From January to March mean temperature is 24° F., while in July, the warmest month, it is 41° F., similar to a London January. Daily range of temperature, 7° F., is small. On an average the warmest day of the summer reaches 62° F. and the coldest night of the winter 7° F. The latter figure is only 1° F. less than that for Balmoral. During the twenty years' record the extremes were 66° F. on June 28, 1902, and 1° F. on January 6, 1894. It will be seen that throughout this period the thermometer never fell to zero. During the severe February of 1895 the lowest temperature was 2° F., which is 19° F. higher than at Braemar in the same month, over 3,000 feet lower down. Thus at times nocturnal cooling in valleys may counterbalance the effect of several thousands of feet in elevation.

Rainfall (much in the form of snow) is heavy, amounting to 160 inches a year, and falls on 263 days. December is the month of heaviest precipitation (19 in.) and June (7½ in.) the least. Snow falls on 170 days a year and no month is free. In December and January snow may be expected to fall on 22 days, and reaches its minimum frequency in July and August, with three days each. In 1885 snow fell on 206 days.

The cold on Ben Nevis has none of the calm, sunny serenity of the high Swiss valleys, such as is characteristic of Davos and St. Moritz. Rather is it a bitter searching cold with high winds lashing the summit, and sending the snow swirling in clouds down the mountain sides. It is indeed a dreary, harsh climate, and science owes a great debt to the observers who lived on the summit and made observations under very trying conditions in order to give us the knowledge we now possess.

The Northern Pennines—(a) Moor House, 1,840 feet

In the Northern Pennines, where the Counties of Yorkshire, Durham, Westmorland and Cumberland converge, is the most consistently elevated mass of land in England. It stretches for many miles without falling below 1,000 feet in altitude, and rises to its highest point in Crossfell, 2,930 feet. The greater part, over 1,200 feet, is untouched moorland and almost uninhabited. It is the coldest part of England.

In 1932 a weather observing station was set up at Moor House, at a height of 1,840 feet, by Mr. Gordon Manley, M.A., M.Sc., President of the Royal Meteorological Society, with the co-operation and help of Durham University, the Leverhulme Research Trustees, the Veteripont Estates, and others.

Moor House is situated in Upper Teesdale on open moorland, being nine miles north-east by north from Appleby and 12 miles west-north-west from Middleton-in-Teesdale. Crossfell lies four miles west-north-west.

The climate is damp, windy and bleak. The temperature records show that the mean annual temperature is 41½° F., or 5° F. lower than at Durham, which is what would be expected allowing for the difference in altitude. The average daily range is 11° F. A July afternoon at Moor House averages 60° F., and mean night temperature is at freezing point or below from December to April. In calm radiation weather the night minimum at Moor House is frequently higher than at Appleby in the valley of the Eden, 1,400 feet lower down.

An interesting feature is that in quiet anticyclonic weather

Photograph by Gordon Manley.

WEATHER HUT ON DUN FELL, 2,735 FEET.
LAKE DISTRICT MOUNTAINS IN DISTANCE, JANUARY 1939.

there are sometimes days when the temperature closely resembles that of the lowlands. On May 5, 1935, Moor House reached 68° F. compared with 71° F. at Appleby and 69° F. at Durham.

The highest temperature recorded at Moor House in ten years was 80° F. on July 10, 1934, and the lowest 0° F. on January 5, 1941. On an average the warmest day of the year is 75° F. and the coldest night 11° F. A broad expanse of high land such as this will have higher afternoon temperature than a solitary peak of the same altitude.

Snow may be expected to lie on the ground on 90 days in the year. Rainfall is about 70 inches per annum. Thunderstorms are sometimes violent and dangerous on the high open moorlands. The monthly mean temperature varies from 33° F. in January and February to 53° F. in July, and closely resembles that of southern Iceland at sea-level. No month is free from the possibility of night frost.

On May 19, 1943, the maximum temperature was as low as 30° F., with snow falling to a depth of a foot, and forming five feet drifts round the house. The chances are considerable that the road leading to the house will be blocked by snowdrifts almost throughout the months of January to March. An attempt has been made to grow potatoes, but they proved to be too small to be worth the trouble. In February, 1941, the resident and his wife took nine hours in a blizzard to cover the six miles from Garrigill to the house, and the last mile and a half meant five hours' struggle. Only very tough people can endure this climate.

The Northern Pennines—(b) Dun Fell, 2,735 feet

In the autumn of 1937 Mr. G. Manley extended his observations by setting up a weather station on Dun Fell (2,780 feet), the second highest summit of the Pennines, and two miles south-south-east from Crossfell. It lies three miles west from Moor House, just described, and 900 feet above it.

Dun Fell is well above the tree-line. Comparatively small increases in elevation can produce a rapid change from the fertile lowlands to sub-Arctic barrenness. This is the highest point at which observations have been made in England. The establishment of the instruments was a task of considerable difficulty, and so was the work of the observers. Mr. Somerville Pattison of Kirkby Thore made a fortnightly climb to the summit throughout the severe winter of 1939-40 to change the chart of the thermograph, an expedition which sometimes meant fifteen miles walking through deep snow.

The data obtained enables us to estimate the mean temperatures. January and February have a mean of 29° F., rising to 49° F. in July and 48° F. in August. The mean temperature is below freezing point from December to March inclusive. Mean annual temperature is 37.7° F. Night frosts total 168 per annum, and on 74 days it will remain continuously below freezing.

Snow covers the ground on approximately 100 days a year, and longer in the drifts. Probably duration of snow-cover would exceed this were not quantities of snow blown from the summit by high winds. In three years the coldest day was January 17, 1940, with a maximum temperature of 14° F. and a minimum of 9° F. In a normal year the warmest day is likely to be 70° F. and the coldest night 15° F.

In exceptional weather a reading of 76° F. was made on June 6, 1939, so that on a mountain top in England at 2,700 feet a temperature may occur which would be rarely reached at sea-level in the Hebrides.

Some remarkable contrasts have been observed in radiation weather. On January 21, 1940, a minimum of 7° F. occurred on the summit, but in the Eden Valley, 2,400 feet below, the thermometer sank to about − 10° F. Mr. E. L. Hawke has shown that in three years of observations the temperature of the coldest night was actually lower in the valley near Rickmansworth than on the summit of Dun Fell in 32 months out of the 36. In December, 1939, the lowest reading on Dun Fell was 17° F., whereas Rickmansworth fell to 4° F.

Sunshine is small on Dun Fell, and on many days the summit is covered in cloud. It has an excessively wet and windy autumn, a variable stormy winter, with long periods of snow-covered ground, high humidity and extremely bitter wind. Spring is cold, and summer short and cloudy. Altogether it is a stern, forbidding climate.

CHAPTER XXI

WHAT CLIMATE HAS YOUR OWN GARDEN?

THAT our climate can vary quite a lot from district to district is clear from the two previous chapters. The divergencies between the Peak of Derbyshire, the Isle of Man and the Fens are marked and obvious. In most parts of the country there are lesser variations about which not so much is known. The study of these local peculiarities is called micro-climatology.

You may live in Lime Tree Avenue. How does the climate in your garden differ from that in your friend Henry Brown's garden in Chestnut Drive half a mile away?

If Brown and yourself live in a town in the fen country the difference may be negligible, but if you live in a hilly or undulating district then quite appreciable differences will occur.

There is the story of the visitor who went to Seathwaite in the Lake District, curious to see England's wettest village. He accosted a passer-by and said, "So this is where you get such a tremendous rainfall?" "Not here," was the reply, "but over in the next field." This anecdote is not so absurd as it appears, for in Borrowdale the rainfall gradient is so pronounced that two points a mile apart may differ in annual rainfall by as much as 25 inches, equal to London's yearly fall.

Variations of temperature are more complex than those of rainfall. Your garden in Lime Tree Avenue may be in a valley, and a late spring frost may ruin your fruit blossom, whereas your friend Brown's garden may be up a hillside where his fruit blossom would escape damage. It has been shown how frost is more severe in a valley than on nearby hills in radiation weather, but even small undulations have their effect.

A meteorologist from the fens visiting Nottingham said, "You are fortunate here; you have several climates." Round Nottingham it was noticed that Attenborough was specially subject to low night temperatures, so its records and those of nearby places were analysed. Attenborough is in the valley of the Trent at a height of 89 feet, and lies 4½ miles south-west of Nottingham Castle at a height of 192 feet. It was discovered that over a period of nine years the night temperature at Attenborough averaged rather

more than 2° F. lower than at Nottingham Castle, but the day
temperature was 1° F. higher. Daily values were examined in
detail for two years. In this period there were as many as 32
nights when the temperature at Attenborough was 7° F. or more
lower than Nottingham. On two occasions the difference was as
great as 10° F. Thus it was established that in the neighbourhood
of Nottingham two places only 4½ miles apart and differing only
100 feet in altitude can vary in temperature on certain nights as
much as a January night at Torquay varies from a night in the
cold high valley of Braemar in Scotland. Perhaps as remarkable

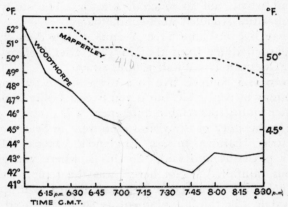

FIG. 35. OCTOBER 1, 1942. TEMPERATURES AT
MAPPERLEY (410 FEET) AND WOODTHORPE (225 FEET),
NOTTS. COMPARATIVE RATE OF TEMPERATURE FALL
ON A HILL TOP AND IN A VALLEY ON A CALM, CLEAR
EVENING

was the discovery that on some hot sunny days Attenborough was
4° F. or 5° F. warmer than Nottingham.

These findings led to experiments in a valley north of
Nottingham. Thermometers were exposed under similar conditions four feet above the ground, one at a height of 225 feet
(30 feet above the valley floor) and one on a neighbouring hill at
410 feet. The two thermometers were 3/4 mile apart. The results
of observations made on October 1, 1942, are shown in Figure 35.
It was a clear still evening after a sunny day with a rising barometer. At 7 p.m. the two thermometers would probably be
similar. Between 7.15 p.m. and 8.45 p.m. the thermometer in
the valley fell 7° F. compared with only 2° F. on the hill-top. The

temperature at the lower level was then 8° F. below that of the higher level.   There is no doubt that this phenomenon is common in fine calm weather in undulating country, as was shown in the remarks on Rickmansworth in Chapter XIX.

A mile from Durham meteorological station is an observing station at Houghall in the valley of the River Wear, at a height of 160 feet and 176 feet lower than Durham.   The minimum at Houghall is occasionally as much as 10° F. lower than at Durham. In the cold February of 1929 the lowest temperature at Durham was 10° F., but Houghall fell to −1° F.

Important investigations were made a few years ago at East Malling Research Station, Kent, by members of the staff and others, and the results incorporated in a paper by C. E. Cornford, B.Sc., A.R.C.S.   It was shown that each type of crop has its own little climate on radiation nights.   Grass produces lower readings than bare soil.   The leaves of grass offer a large surface for radiation, while at the same time the air trapped among them insulates the leaves from the warmth of the ground, much as cellular underwear insulates the human body from temperature changes.

Up the slope of a hill is the best site for fruit trees.   The hilltop is most free from frost but is not recommended because it is more liable to wind than a situation partly down the slope.

Anyone living in undulating country who is interested in meteorology would find the exploration of night temperatures of hills and valleys a fascinating subject.

These are natural local differences.   Large towns produce artificial differences.   Perhaps the most noteworthy is that night temperatures are higher in towns than they would be were the site open country.   Towns also affect the depth of snow lying.

CHAPTER XXII

THE WEATHER AFFECTS YOU PHYSICALLY

WE are linked to the weather throughout our lives. Some philosophers wonder whether anything material can exist unless there is a mind to perceive it. It would certainly be sad if the pageant of the weather were to pass unnoticed in an uninhabited world. The weather can brace or relax us, exhilarate or depress us. Try as we may we cannot be indifferent.

These effects occur to us at once, and others, too. A great flood causes devastation, loss of life, epidemics, and lack of food. A long drought causes the failure of essential crops, bringing famine and death to thousands. People may die from exposure to bitter cold, or from the heat of a torrid sun.

Such events affect us little in our favoured islands. There are, however, less sensational though quite important effects which concern us all.

Everyone is affected by the variations of heat and cold. The body is like an engine. It generates its own heat by burning or digesting the food we eat, and its temperature must be kept at about 98.4° F. for health. In our climate for most of the year the combustion of food in the body is not sufficient to keep us warm, so we wear clothing to slow down the loss of heat, and warm our houses for the same purpose. In summer we need less clothing and would probably be better if we wore even less than we do. In this respect women are more fortunate than men, as custom decrees that they may wear flimsy dresses. Many women oppose any attempt on the part of their husbands to adopt more reasonable clothing on the ground that it is unusual, or "not done." Perhaps when education advances beyond the primitive stage we shall shed these conventional absurdities.

The body regulates its heat largely by the skin. In cold weather the surface blood-vessels contract and so the conduction of heat to the skin and hence to the air is checked. In heat the surface vessels dilate enabling the surplus heat to reach the skin and pass away into the air. Perspiration helps to cool the body as it produces a "wet-bulb" effect as it evaporates from the skin.

In hot air perspiration is considerable. At rest it may be imperceptible, say about one-twentieth of a pint per hour. It has been estimated that when running the rate of loss is about 2½ pints an hour, and during football nine pints. A cricketer playing all day at Cairo in warm conditions would part with about 17 pints before stumps were drawn.

Though a healthy person can endure great extremes of heat and cold the most favourable limits of the thermometer are from 50° F. to 75° F. In the English midlands the maximum temperature will fall within these limits on about 220 days in a year, with about 20 days over 75° F. and 125 days below 50° F. When the thermometer soars to 80° F. or more one feels less energetic and clerks in banks and offices will be more liable to make mistakes. Very low temperatures also reduce vitality.

In winter, warming of houses is universal, but as yet few houses have any means of cooling the air in summer. This is no doubt due to the fact that intense heat is not common in this country and is rarely protracted. The solidly-built Victorian house will keep cooler in summer than the modern house, and winter cold penetrates more slowly. In the course of time our houses will be built in a way that will afford heat insulation. When this comes we shall need less fuel to warm them in winter, and in summer our rooms will remain cooler in a heat wave. Central heating of corridors and bedrooms keeps them at an even temperature, but for living-rooms a fire is best as it helps to ventilate the room.

In hot summer weather a room is best kept cool by a white sun blind *outside* the window so that the sun's rays do not reach the glass. Windows should be opened in the morning when the air is cool, but closed during the heat of the afternoon. If the temperature outside is 80° F. and in the room 70° F., then opening the windows will raise the temperature in the room. Temperature changes in unheated rooms of a house are much smaller than outdoors. Investigations made by the author over a period of years in a bedroom of a modern house facing south-east showed that the temperature in the bedroom varied by about one-third of the amount in the thermometer screen outside. A range of 20° F. between day and night outside would produce a range of about 7° F. in the bedroom. It is not advisable to overheat rooms in winter. They may feel drowsily comfortable, but they increase the body's susceptibility to a "chill." Plumbing should be so

K

arranged that the pipes are protected from cold. The old fallacy still seems to exist that thawing bursts the pipes. Pipes are burst on freezing, but it is not apparent till a thaw sets in.

The author took a friend who lived in the cellarless flats of Eastern England down a cellar on a hot summer day with the thermometer at 80° F., and asked him to guess the temperature. He thought it must be near freezing point. He was then shown the thermometer, which registered 60° F. It was the rapid change in temperature as one descended into the cellar that made it feel cold. In the hot summer of 1933 a record of temperature was kept at Nottingham in a cellar under a private house. It was perfectly dry as the soil was sandstone. The highest temperature recorded in this cellar during 1933 was 65° F., and the lowest 36° F., compared with the outside air which ranged from 88° F. to 22° F. In July, day temperature in the cellar averaged 61° F., the entrance hall of the house 70° F., a bedroom 71° F., and the outside air 74° F. Attics under slate roofs become very hot in summer but are very cold in winter.

Most people have summer and winter underwear, which they put on or discard by the calendar, as though it were a religious rite. Thin summer underwear is beneficial; it increases the vitality of the skin. It is well to wear thin under-garments as long as possible into the autmn. Thick winter underwear is not a protection against illness. It devitalises the skin and robs it of its natural power of reacting to temperature changes. The thicker the winter underwear the more sensitive becomes the skin to cold, and one develops a "nesh" feeling. The old chest-protector of the Victorians was about as good a device for weakening the chest as it was possible to invent. The case of elderly people is rather different. Their vitality is lower; the reaction of their skin to temperature changes is more feeble. They will usually need thicker underwear than the young or middle-aged. Exercise will keep a healthy person warm in the coldest weather, but the eating of ices has little effect in hot weather, apart from the pleasant sensation of coolness in the mouth.

Humidity plays an important part in bodily comfort. A temperature of 90° F., with a humidity of 85 per cent. would feel intolerable, but in the very dry air of Khartoum a temperature of 100° F. is comparatively bearable. In England air at a temperature of 70° F., almost saturated after a thunderstorm, would feel very heavy and oppressive, but the same temperature with a low humidity of 25 per cent. would have a sensation of cool freshness.

Wind is an important factor in comfort. Still air feels warmer than moving air at the same temperature. Warm, moist air in front of a depression is devitalising, but the drier cooler air in its rear increases the metabolism of the body and is energising. In hot weather dark-coloured clothing is warmer than light-coloured, and white is the coolest. Dark colours absorb the heat of the sun and transfer it to the body but white reflects much of the heat. At most temperatures a breeze is beneficial, but with the thermometer at 40° F. or less it causes discomfort. Air at 25° F. may be quite comfortable if it is calm, but would feel bitterly cold with a wind.

If the temperature falls quickly in the evening the windows of a house will often "steam" inside. This is because the glass falls to the temperature of the outside air or nearly, and if this is below the dew-point of the air in the room this dew or "steam" forms. A sudden thaw will cause "steaming" on the *outside* of windows of unheated rooms. The air of the room has become cold during the frost and so is below the dew-point of the newly-arrived warm air outside. The dew or "steam" on a window always occurs on the side of the window where the air is warmer. Sometimes in a sudden thaw wallpaper in an unheated room will show wet patches. This is caused by the walls being below the dew-point in temperature in regard to the warmer air. As soon as the temperature of the room and its walls rises the signs of damp will disappear. It is not damp "coming out of the walls," as one hears it said, nor does it mean that the house is damp.

Do not be afraid of rain or damp. So long as one's clothing is kept dry and feet warm it will do no harm. A damp, mild winter is more healthy than a cold, dry one in England, in spite of popular beliefs to the contrary. Fog, in towns, is charged with smoke particles and other impurities, which can irritate the lungs. A sea mist is harmless. Our blustery rainy south-west wind is healthy in winter. The dry, piercing east wind is not healthy in winter and spring. Contrary to popular belief, very warm weather is not health-giving. Eighty degrees and over in the shade is apt to "race the engine" and wear us out too soon. Compare the fresh youthfulness of an Englishwoman of thirty years old with the faded air of a woman of the same age in a hot country.

The ultra-violet rays of the sun are beneficial. They are most abundant on the coast and at sea. Inland, near large towns, much ultra-violet light is cut off by smoke.

It is commonly supposed that cold weather keeps down an epidemic by destroying bacteria. There is little ground for this belief. The germs of disease may be rendered more or less inert by frost, but they become lively enough and flourish exceedingly in heated rooms, and it is in heated rooms where germs are so easily passed from one person to another.

Our British climate, with its winds from the Atlantic Ocean, its freedom from excessive heat and cold, is a wonderfully healthy one. The human race has reached its highest development in the cooler countries such as Britain and Scandinavia. From these countries went the pioneers who founded the civilisation of North America. The British race owes an everlasting debt of gratitude to the climate of these islands.

Let us leave those warm, sun-drenched climates of the south to the idle Lotus eaters. Ours is a man's climate; yes, and a woman's too!

CHAPTER XXIII.

THE WEATHER AFFECTS YOU MENTALLY

A GOOD deal has been written and said of late years about the influence of mind over matter, especially regarding the human body. One is apt, therefore, to overlook the great influence that the state of the body has on the mind. Weather, as we have seen, affects us physically, and bodily sensations produce mental reactions.

A simple example is the cheering effect of a fine day and the depressing result of a wet one. A business man irritated by a wet journey to his office may dismiss a clerk for some trivial fault, thus upsetting the whole economy of the clerk's life and thought. A person suffering from a cold in the head may be so dominated by it that even sunshine fails to cheer him. A heat wave accompanied by a humid atmosphere is a physical strain, and this puts one's nerves on edge. Even dry heat may produce fatigue and have the same result. People with plenty of vitality feel this least, and those who are "run-down" suffer most. Fog depresses the mind.

These are simple effects of the weather; there are others which are more subtle.

The memory has a distinct tendency to recall the spectacular and unusual and to forget the ordinary. Thus elderly people tend to remember severe winters and forget mild ones, and as a result when they look back on their youth all winters seem severe in recollection. This is part of the reason why we hear references to "old-fashioned" winters. The author's memories of the summers of his schooldays between the ages of ten and sixteen are of hot, sunny days with the grass burnt brown. It was rather disconcerting, therefore, to turn up official records and find that five out of these seven summers were cooler than the average. Obviously, the hot spells were impressed on the memory and the rest was forgotten. The truth is that none of us can rely very much on memories of weather that is past.

A doctor once said "Present pain is always the worst." This is not literally true, but the germ of truth behind it is due to the dulling of the memory of past pain, while the nerves of the body are only too vividly aware of the present ache.

Suppose it rains intensely in a thunderstorm. It is quite common to hear people say, "I've never seen it rain so heavily before." In most cases they have, on quite a number of occasions. They can actually see the present deluge, but past downpours have grown dim in the memory. The same psychological reaction occurs during great heat or cold. "I've never known it so hot," or, "I've never felt such cold." Similarly, you may hear sailors say, "I've never seen such a storm in my life," or "I've been forty years at sea and never seen such a gale," or "It was the worst crossing for fifty years." Now such statements may be right, but more often the sight of the present storm is overshadowing recollection of past ones. Anyone with a scientific training will be on guard when he hears statements like these; he will want factual evidence to substantiate them.

Another factor may play an unconscious part. Some newspapers and advertisements have a way of keeping the mind keyed up to expect the unprecedented and the amazing. As a result it may happen that the statement of a scientific fact which is really more remarkable than many a headline, fails to impress the minds of the public. Recall the person (page 28) who "would not have been surprised if five inches of rain had fallen." He would not have been surprised at five feet, either. Indeed, nothing would have surprised him, because he had not got a "yard-stick" in his mind which would enable him to judge what an inch of rain meant. That is why I have mentioned "yard-sticks" in the chapters on rainfall. Similarly, on a hot day I am sometimes asked, "What has the temperature reached?" I reply 85 degrees, or whatever it is, and get the retort, "Oh, I should not have been surprised if you had said 185° F." Of course, human life would soon cease in a temperature of 185° F.

Some of us like to regard our climate as a bad one; almost with pride. A lady visiting the continent for the first time left England during unsettled, showery weather. When she arrived at the Hook of Holland the weather was squally, clouds careered across the sky and rain fell in heavy showers. "This is most disappointing." she remarked, "I thought when we got out of England we should leave English weather behind." Britain has not the sole patent rights to bad weather. Fog can be dense in France. Our troops in sunny Italy during the war discovered that the sun did not always shine there by any means.

That the weather changes with the moon is an old belief

which is taking a long time to die. Scientific observation shows there are no grounds for this belief. The weather may, on occasion, change with the moon, just as it may change when you change your socks. Dear Aunt Bessie may revoke at whist at 10 o'clock next Tuesday, and at the same moment lightning may kill a cow in a field a hundred miles away. It would be very rash to assume that Aunt Bessie's lapse had caused the death of the cow, or that the death of the cow caused her deplorable fault, without very definite data to support either assumption. After all, the moon is continually "changing," not just once a week as the almanacs have it. In scientific investigation strict impartiality must be observed. The interested observer, being a normal human being, is apt to notice facts which seem to confirm his belief and ignore those which contradict it.

Another old belief is that frost is most severe when there is a moon. This, too, has no scientific basis. To test this idea the author examined his own meteorological observations for five winters, 1939-40, 1940-41, 1941-42, 1942-43, and 1943-44, the winter period being taken as November to March. The seven days comprised by full moon and the three nights before and after were taken as the "moonlight period." The temperatures of these nights were compared with those of the remainder of the months concerned. Over the five winters the mean minimum temperature of the "moonlight nights" was 33.1° F., and for the rest of the time it was just the same. The coldest night of the month occurred in the "moonlight period" on six occasions, and in other parts of the month on nineteen occasions. Now, probability alone, or the throw of the dice, would give us this result, that is the coldest night of any month in the moonlight period in one month out of every four.

It is pretty widely thought that English summers, to be worth the name, should be hot and dry. If July and August are about normal in temperature and rainfall, the public are apt to be dissatisfied. They will say it has not been much of a summer. Summer is visualised as a succession of brilliantly sunny days with an afternoon temperature in the eighties. But such conditions are appropriate to Southern France, and are abnormal in Britain. When we do get weather of this type it does not, as a rule, last long.

Yet another old belief is that if the wind is in a cold quarter on March 21st, it will remain in that quarter (with generally cold weather) for three months. If this were true we could make some nice long forecasts. But it has no basis in fact, and in our climate of variable winds such constancy of wind direction does not occur.

"No more Torquay for me," said a gentleman. "We spent a week there and it rained all the time. We went to Exmouth this year and had beautiful weather."

This statement was actually made to the author. What is so odd is that it did not seem to have occurred to this gentleman that during the wet week at Torquay it would also be rainy at Exmouth, and that during the beautifully fine week at Exmouth it would be fine at Torquay. One may strike a bad patch of weather while on holiday anywhere in Britain, even on the dry East Coast, or one may experience a fine period in the rainy Lake District.

Everyone who has some knowledge of a subject has met the person who can tell him all about it. Meteorologists are no exception. We meet the man, knowing nothing of meteorological science, who dogmatically enunciates ridiculous fallacies as though they were pearls of wisdom. One is always pleased to give information to those who wish to learn, but this type of man will not listen to facts; he "knows it all."

We have seen how unreliable memory can be for weather long past, and this same thing is even true for shorter periods. The spring of 1943 was very dry. "Have you ever known so dry a spring?" I was asked. "Yes," I replied. "In 1938 we had the driest spring of the present century.

Yes, there was some truth in the doctor's remark. "Present pain is always the worst," and we may paraphrase it as "Present cold is always the most biting," or "It never rains but it pours."

CHAPTER XXIV.

"AND WILL IT RAIN TO-MORROW?"

THE inevitable question which any meteorologist is asked is "Will it rain to-morrow?" People are most inconsiderate in this matter. Fortunately, a meteorologist can read the official forecast and pass it on. During the war this simple solution was not possible and he had to do what he could from his own knowledge.

The isolated observer must watch the sky, the wind, the barometer and the thermometer. If he notices the barometer is falling with a freshening south-east wind and a muddy sky he may deduce that a depression is advancing from the Atlantic, and will probably bring unsettled weather and rain. He will not know how large the depression is or whether it is a vigorous one, or filling up and dying. A useful rule is Buys Ballot's law, which says that "if you stand with your back to the wind, pressure is lower on your left hand than on your right." With a west wind it is more unsettled in the north than in the south. A north wind means low pressure over the North Sea, and Eastern England will be less fine than the West. With an east wind weather will be poor in the south, and with a south wind conditions will be finer in the east than in the west.

Popular weather sayings are not always true. The legend of bad weather and St. Swithin's Day does not hold water. "When March comes in like a lion, it goes out like a lamb," will not bear testing. "Rain before seven, fine at eleven," is just another way of saying that rain is not often prolonged, at least over Eastern Britain.

A clear moon is said to presage night frost. The truth is that conditions favourable to night frost often produce a clear moon, if there happens to be one about.

Much has been written about Buchan's cold and warm spells, and even to-day meteorologists are not altogether agreed about them. These so-called spells are as follows:—

Cold periods	Warm periods
February 7 to 10	July 12 to 15
April 11 to 14	August 12 to 15
May 9 to 14	December 3 to 9
June 29 to July 4	
August 6 to 11	
November 6 to 12	

Test them for yourselves. A most interesting little book on these spells is "Buchan's Days," by E. L. Hawke. There is a high probability of a warm spell, with days exceeding the normal July temperature, in the second half of May. This spell has appeared in England in 22 out of the last 30 years.

The old saying that a green Christmas makes a fat churchyard is untrue if it suggests that mild weather in winter is unhealthy. A snowy, foggy Christmas, or one with a raw east wind is more likely to fill the churchyard.

The most accurate forecasts possible are those made by the Meteorological Office. Into this office a vast mass of information is continually pouring from Britain, Europe and the Atlantic

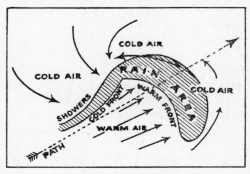

FIG. 36. DIAGRAM OF A DEPRESSION.

Ocean. This information is drawn on synoptic charts. Having a series of the charts and studying the changes which are taking place the forecast department decide what immediate changes are likely in the future.

The two main factors in our weather changes are the "depression," or area of low barometer, and the anticyclone or "high." Figure 36 shows the modern view of the structure of a depression. A depression is a system of closed isobars with pressure lowest in the centre. They vary enormously in size, and may be more than a thousand miles in diameter. Weather is unsettled with rain and probably wind. No two depressions are alike, which complicates the fine art of forecasting.

A "secondary depression" is an offspring of a main depression. Sometimes it is more vigorous than the parent depression with severe gales on its southern side.

An anticyclone brings quiet fair weather. In spring and summer the weather is frequently brilliantly fine and often warm, but in winter it may be continuously overcast and depressing with little or no rain. In winter, too, fog may develop, and in autumn, morning fogs may be dense, giving place to a fine sunny day.

Forecasting is too great a subject to deal with in this book, other than superficially. The reader should not fail to study the details of forecasting in "The Weather Map," and in W. H. Pick's "Short Course in Elementary Meteorology." Both these little books may be obtained from His Majesty's Stationery Office.

CHAPTER XXV.

KEEPING YOUR OWN WEATHER RECORD.

IF you are interested in the world as the Creator made it, one of the most interesting things you can do is to keep a record of the weather where you live. I hope that reading this little book has made you wish to do so.

A weather record may be a very simple affair, just a diary of notes each day. It is much more satisfying and useful to make instrumental observations. The interest in one's own record increases the longer the record becomes, for when unusual weather arrives one can turn back to see how long it is since anything comparable occurred.

If one lives in a locality where no official record is kept, then your observations may be useful to the Meteorological Office. Every observer should have a barometer and a rain gauge. Standard mercurial barometers as used by the Meteorological Office are rather expensive, but a good aneroid will answer the purpose of an amateur very well. It should be adjusted against a standard barometer, and it also requires correction for height above sea-level. All barometer readings are reduced to sea-level to be comparable.

Your rain-gauge should be of a standard type, such as the Meteorological Office or Snowdon pattern, with a deep funnel for holding snow. The gauge should be set up in an open position on a grass lawn, well away from trees and buildings. The ideal is for a gauge to be twice as far away from an object as the object's height, such as ten feet or more away from a five feet wall. An amateur once set up a gauge only a foot away from a four feet wall and wondered why his readings were all wrong. A rain-gauge should be examined once a day at 9 a.m. G.M.T., or as near that hour as is convenient. The water in the gauge, if any, should be measured and the amount entered to the previous day. That is, if you measure 0.14 inch of rain at 9 a.m. on the 16th, you must enter this amount in your register as the rainfall for the 15th.

The Meteorological Office welcomes regular rainfall readings, and the knowledge we have of rainfall over Britain depends in great degree on the work of voluntary observers.

Your next step is to make instrumental readings of temperature. It is no use exposing a thermometer on a fence or against a wall. It will read incorrectly. One needs a standard screen as used by the Meteorological Office, and thermometers should be standard also, with a certificate from the National Physical Laboratory. The screen should be set up on a lawn well away from trees and buildings. You will need two thermometers, a maximum for registering the highest temperature in the 24 hours and a minimum for recording the lowest. Inaccurate readings are of no value to yourself or anyone else, so that is why standard conditions are stressed.

The two thermometers are read once a day at 9 a.m. when you visit the rain-gauge. They are read and set as described on page 46.

So much for the essentials for a weather record. You can add other instruments as you please.

Some non-instrumental observations should be made as well, such as the direction and estimated force of the wind and the amount of cloud. Notes on the general weather should be added, including fog, snow, hail and thunderstorms.

Even amateur observers will need a "book of words," and should obtain the "Meteorological Observer's Handbook" (H.M. Stationery Office) or "Hints to Meteorological Observers" (Royal Meteorological Society).

Some people ask: what is the use of a mass of figures? Figures as such are not interesting; it is what they stand for and mean that is important. Another common question is: What is the use of keeping a weather record? This can be answered by putting another question: How long is it since it was as warm as it is to-day? The latter question and many others like it could not be answered if records were not carefully kept. What is more important is that virtually all our knowledge of our climate (or any other) is due to the faithful work of observers. All means and averages are computed from their observations. Do you wish to help?

If you live on a hill and your friend is in a near-by valley you could obtain valuable information on the relation between valley and hill temperatures if each of you kept a record with a standard screen.

We do not know enough about snowfall. Your observations

on this would be useful especially if you live on high ground, or in a mountainous district.

From time to time a weather observer will have a red-letter day, when something really unusual happens.

The author remembers the thrill he experienced when on June 1st, 1936, the minimum thermometer in the screen fell to 30.7° F., the only June frost he had recorded. Other highlights were 70° F. on March 27, 1929, a summer day of 68° F. on November 5, 1938, and an August night of 34° F. in 1940. Individual months will stand out in one's register, such as the record warmth of March, 1938, or the intense cold of January, 1940. What observer will forget the three very dry months of February, March and April, 1938, when the author recorded rainfalls of only 0.75 inch, 0.13 inch, and 0.06 inch respectively. The author's gauge showed no rain from April 5th to May 11th, a period of 37 days.

Millions of people live their whole lives in Britain and know no more of its climate than is contained in a few ridiculous superstitions and fallacies. What a tragedy that is!

Many interests in life which seemed so important once, lose colour and fade with time, but the weather observer possesses a heritage which can be a source of happiness for ever. Observing the weather helps to keep one young, for weather changes hold the secret of perpetual youth.

THIS WEATHER OF OURS

For Further Reading

The Weather Map. H.M. Stationery Office.

W. H. PICK: A Short Course in Elementary Meteorology. H.M. Stationery Office.

SIR NAPIER SHAW: The Drama of Weather. Cambridge University Press.

E. L. HAWKE: Buchan's Days. Lovat Dickson Ltd.

E. G. BILHAM: The Climate of the British Isles. Macmillan & Co.

D. BRUNT: Weather Study. Nelson.

G. KIMBLE AND R. BUSH: The Weather. Pelican.

M. DE CARLE S. SALTER: The Rainfall of the British Isles. University of London Press.

Rainfall Atlas of the British Isles. Royal Meteorological Society.

J. H. WILLIS: Weatherwise. George Allen & Unwin.

For Observers

Meteorological Observer's Handbook. H.M. Stationery Office.

W. MARRIOTT: Hints to Meteorological Observers. Royal Meteorological Society.

In following current weather the following are invaluable:

Daily Weather Report of the Meteorological Office. Meteorological Office.

Monthly Weather Report of the Meteorological Office. H.M. Stationery Office.

An excellent book for younger readers:

DOROTHY FISK: The Sun, the Sky, and Kit. Faber & Faber.

WILLIAM ALEXANDER: The Junior Officers' Handbook on weather. George Allen & Unwin Ltd.

W. J. D. ALLEN AND WILLIAM ALEXANDER: The Observers' Book on Meteorology. George Allen & Unwin Ltd.

GEORGE ALLEN & UNWIN LTD
LONDON: 40 MUSEUM STREET, W.C.1
CAPE TOWN: 58–60 LONG STREET
TORONTO: 91 WELLINGTON STREET WEST
BOMBAY: 15 GRAHAM ROAD, BALLARD ESTATE
CALCUTTA: 17 CENTRAL AVENUE, P.O. DHARAMTALA,
WELLINGTON, N.Z.: 8 KINGS CRESCENT, LOWER HUTT
SYDNEY, N.S.W.: BRADBURY HOUSE, 55 YORK STREET